Food Tables & Labelling

and

David A Bender
Senior Lecturer
Dept of Biochemistry and Molecular Biology
University College London

OXFORD
UNIVERSITY PRESS

OXFORD
UNIVERSITY PRESS

Great Clarendon Street, Oxford OX2 6DP

Oxford University Press is a department of the University of Oxford.
It furthers the University's objective of excellence in research, scholarship,
and education by publishing worldwide in

Oxford New York
Athens Auckland Bangkok Bogotá Buenos Aires Calcutta
Cape Town Chennai Dar es Salaam Delhi Florence Hong Kong Istanbul
Karachi Kuala Lumpur Madrid Melbourne Mexico City Mumbai
Nairobi Paris São Paulo Singapore Taipei Tokyo Toronto Warsaw

with associated companies in
Berlin Ibadan

Oxford is a registered trade mark of Oxford University Press in the UK
and in certain other countries

British Library Cataloguing in Publication Data

Data available

ISBN 0 19 832814 1 (school edition)
      0 19 832815 X (bookshop edition)

This publication contains Crown copyright material from the
Compostion of Foods 5th edition and its Supplements and has been reproduced
under licence from the Controller of her Majesty's Stationery Office.

Typeset and designed by Mike Brain Graphic Design Ltd.

Printed and bound in Great Britain by Butler & Tanner Ltd. Frome and
London

Contents

Preface

This book provides a straightforward guide to the composition of fresh and manufactured foods, and the information that appears on food labels. These tables will be of value to the general reader and teachers, college students and school pupils, from Key Stage 3 of the National Curriculum through GCSE, A-Level, and NVQ, to GNVQ, diploma, and degree courses. They may be used to support work in home economics, food technology, chemistry, biology and other subjects that involve nutrition and food science.

The tables and explanatory notes are arranged in seven sections:

- The need for food: energy and protein requirements

- The need for food: vitamins and minerals

- The nutrient content of foods

- Alcoholic beverages

- Food labelling

- Height, weight and growth

- Miscellaneous tables, including equivalence of metric, Imperial and household measures, and equivalence of temperatures.

There are specimen calculations at various levels.

More comprehensive background information will be found in:

Bender, AE & Bender, DA. *A Dictionary of Food and Nutrition*, Oxford University Press, 1995

Bender, DA. *Introduction to Nutrition and Metabolism*, 2nd Edition, Taylor and Francis, London, 1997.

More detailed information on the nutrient content of foods (both a wider range of nutrients than is shown here and also a greater number of foods) is available in:

McCance and Widdowson's The Composition of Foods, 5th Edition, Royal Society of Chemistry and Ministry of Agriculture, Fisheries and Food, 1991, and supplements to the 4th and 5th editions.

You will also find a great deal of useful information on the following Internet/World Wide Web pages:

- Arbor Communications: guide to nutrition resource on the Internet: http://netspace.net.au/%7Ehelmant/nutid.htm

- Department of Health: http://www.open.gov.uk/doh/dhhome.htm

- Food and Nutrition Information Center (US Department of Agriculture): http://www.nal.usda.gov/fnic/

- International Union of Nutritional Sciences: http://www.monash.edu.au/IUNS/

- Martindale's Health Science Guide: Virtual Nutrition Center: http://www-sci.lib.uci.edu/HSG/Nutrition.html#PP1

- Ministry of Agriculture, Fisheries and Food: http://www.maff.gov.uk/

- Tufts University Nutrition Navigator: http://navigator.tufts.edu

- United Nations Food and Agriculture Organization: http://www.fao.org/

- World Health Organization: http://www.who.ch/

A suite of computer programs for Windows® 3.x and Windows® 95/98 is available to accompany this book. Titled *The Foods You Eat*, the programs permit calculation of energy requirements, calculation of the nutrient content of the foods listed in this book, comparison of meals and diets with Reference Nutrient Intakes, and selection of foods that are rich sources of nutrients. For further information about the computer programs, please contact Dr David A Bender, Dept of Biochemistry and Molecular Biology, University College London, Gower Street, London WC1E 6BT, or by email to dab@biochem.ucl.ac.uk.

Tables 22 and 23 in this publication contain Crown copyright material from *The Composition of Foods*, 5th edition, and its Supplements, which has been reproduced under licence from the Controller of Her Majesty's Stationery Office.

A) The need for food: energy and protein

The food we eat must supply us with enough energy to meet the needs for maintenance of the body and physical activity, but not too much, since excess is stored in the body as fat, and excess body fat can be hazardous to health. It must also supply enough protein to meet our needs for growth and repair, and the 13 vitamins and 25 or so minerals that are essential for normal functioning of the body.

Units of energy

The most commonly used unit of energy in nutrition is the **calorie**. One calorie is the amount of heat required to raise the temperature of 1 ml of water through 1 degree Celsius (precisely, from 14.5°C to 15.5°C). One calorie is a very small amount of energy, and in nutrition we use the kilocalorie (1,000 cal, sometimes written as Cal, but more correctly shown as kcal).

The correct SI (Système Internationale d'Unités) unit of energy is the **joule**; in nutrition we use kilojoules (kJ, 1,000 J) and megajoules (MJ, 1,000,000 J). Note that the megajoule has a capital M (MJ), while the kilojoule has a small k (kJ). Because both calories and joules are in widespread use, both are used in this book, just as both are shown on food labels.

The relationship between calories and joules is:

1 cal = 4.186 J (normally rounded off to 4.2)

1 J = 0.2389 cal (normally rounded off to 0.24)

To convert calories to joules, multiply by 4.186 (or 4.2)

To convert joules to calories, divide by 4.186 (or 4.2).

Energy expenditure and energy needs

For an adult, food must provide an amount of energy equal to that expended in maintaining the body and physical activity. For a child or pregnant woman, there is an additional energy requirement to meet the cost of growth, and for a breast-feeding mother there is an additional requirement to meet the cost of producing and secreting the milk.

An energy intake greater than expenditure leads to the excess being stored as fat, while an energy intake less than expenditure leads to loss of weight, emaciation, and eventually death. We can therefore determine energy requirements on the basis of energy expenditure.

The energy cost of maintaining the body is the **Basal Metabolic Rate (BMR)**. It is the energy required for turnover of body tissues, heart action to circulate the blood, breathing, and the activity of nerves and the brain. BMR is measured under strictly controlled conditions of temperature (so that energy is not being expended to keep warm or cool down), some hours after a meal (so that energy is not being expended on digestion and absorption), awake, but completely at rest. It is thus the energy you would expend if you lay flat on your back all day, doing nothing; on average BMR is about 60 percent of total energy expenditure.

Basal Metabolic Rate is determined by the amount of metabolically active tissue on the body (mainly muscle). It therefore depends on body weight, gender (because women have larger reserves of fat, and therefore less muscle, than men of the same body weight), and age (because even if there is no change in body weight, there is a gradual replacement of muscle by fat with increasing age). Table 1 shows BMR at various ages and body weights in kcal/day, and Table 2 in MJ/day.

The energy cost of physical activity is most usually expressed as a **Physical Activity Ratio (PAR)** – the ratio of the energy cost of performing the activity : BMR. As shown in Table 3, PAR ranges from about 1.2 x BMR for gentle activities up to almost 8 x BMR for very vigorous activities. Table 4 shows the classification of different types of work by the average PAR of that work through the 8 hour working day.

Table 1 Basal metabolic rate, kcal/day

		body weight (kg)				
		50	60	70	80	90
males	age 10–17	1524	1699	1874	2049	2224
	age 18–29	1443	1596	1749	1902	2054
	age 30–59	1456	1572	1688	1804	1919
	age over 60	1162	1297	1432	1567	1702
females	age 10–17	1355	1476	1598	1720	1842
	age 18–29	1231	1378	1525	1672	1819
	age 30–59	1264	1351	1438	1525	1612
	age over 60	1119	1224	1329	1434	1539

Table 2 Basal metabolic rate, MJ/day

		body weight (kg)				
		50	60	70	80	90
males	age 10–17	6.38	7.11	7.84	8.58	9.31
	age 18–29	6.04	6.68	7.32	7.96	8.60
	age 30–59	6.10	6.58	7.07	7.55	8.04
	age over 60	4.86	5.43	6.00	6.56	7.12
females	age 10–17	5.67	6.18	6.69	7.20	7.71
	age 18–29	5.16	5.77	6.39	7.00	7.62
	age 30–59	5.29	5.65	6.02	6.38	6.75
	age over 60	4.68	5.12	5.56	6.00	6.44

Table 3 Energy cost of physical activity, expressed as physical activity ratio (PAR = multiple of basal metabolic rate)

PAR	
1.0–1.4	Lying, standing or sitting at rest, e.g. watching TV, reading, writing, using a computer, eating, playing cards and board games
1.5–1.8	*sitting:* sewing, knitting, playing piano, driving
	standing: preparing vegetables, washing dishes, ironing, general office and laboratory work
1.9–2.4	*standing:* mixed household chores, cooking, playing snooker or bowls
2.5–3.3	*standing:* dressing, undressing, showering, making beds, vacuum cleaning
	walking: 3–4 km/h, playing cricket
	occupational: tailoring, shoemaking, electrical and machine tool industry, painting and decorating
3.4–4.4	*standing:* mopping floors, gardening, cleaning windows, table tennis, sailing
	walking: 4–6 km/h, playing golf
	occupational: motor vehicle repairs, carpentry and joinery, chemical industry, bricklaying
4.5–5.9	*standing:* polishing furniture, chopping wood, heavy gardening, volley ball
	walking: 6–7 km/h
	exercise: dancing, moderate swimming, gentle cycling, slow jogging
	occupational: labouring, hoeing, road construction, digging and shovelling, felling trees
6.0–7.9	*walking:* uphill with load or cross-country, climbing stairs
	exercise: jogging, cycling, energetic swimming, skiing, tennis, football

Table 4 Classification of work by physical activity ratio (PAR = multiple of basal metabolic rate) for an 8 hour working day, excluding leisure activities

	PAR		
	men	women	
Light	1.7	1.7	professional, clerical and technical workers, administrative and managerial staff, sales representatives
Moderate	2.7	2.2	sales staff, domestic work, students, transport workers, joiners, roofing workers
Moderately heavy	3.0	2.3	machine operators, labourers, agricultural workers, forestry, hunting and fishing, bricklaying and masonry
Heavy	3.8	2.8	labourers, agricultural workers, bricklaying, masonry where there is little or no mechanization

Total energy expenditure (and hence energy requirement) can be calculated from the overall **Physical Activity Level (PAL)**, which is the sum of the PAR x time spent in each type of activity through the day. Tables 5 and 6 show how total energy expenditure and PAL can be calculated from an activity diary in which you record the time spent in each type of activity through the day.

A desirable Physical Activity Level, in terms of health, is 1.7 x BMR; the average PAL of adults in Britain is only about 1.4 x BMR, suggesting that many people do very little physical exercise outside their work.

Table 5

Specimen activity diary for a person age 25, weighing 70 kg and 175 cm tall, who has a calculated BMR = 1750 kcal/day = 1750 ÷ 24 = 73 kcal/hour

activity	PAR	kcal/h	hours spent	kcal total
sleeping	1.0	1.0 x 73 = 73	8	8.0 x 73 = 584
sitting	1.1	1.1 x 73 = 80	4	4.0 x 80 = 320
standing	1.5	1.5 x 73 = 110	4	4.0 x 110 = 440
light work	2.0	2.0 x 73 = 146	3	3.0 x 146 = 438
medium work	2.8	2.8 x 73 = 204	2.5	2.5 x 204 = 510
hard work/light exercise	3.8	3.8 x 73 = 277	1.5	1.5 x 277 = 416
moderate exercise	5.0	5.0 x 73 = 365	0.5	0.5 x 365 = 183
heavy exercise	6.7	6.7 x 73 = 490	0.5	0.5 x 490 = 245
TOTAL			**24**	**3136**

Overall Physical Activity Level = total energy expenditure ÷ BMR = 3136 ÷ 1750 = 1.79

Table 6

Specimen activity diary for a person age 25, weighing 70 kg and 175 cm tall, who has a calculated BMR = 7.32 MJ/day = 7.32 ÷ 24 = 0.305 MJ/hour

activity	PAR	MJ /h	hours spent	MJ total
sleeping	1.0	1.0 x 0.305 = 0.305	8	8.0 x 0.305 = 2.440
sitting	1.1	1.1 x 0.305 = 0.336	4	4.0 x 0.336 = 1.344
standing	1.5	1.5 x 0.305 = 0.458	4	4.0 x 0.458 = 1.832
light work	2.0	2.0 x 0.305 = 0.610	3	3.0 x 0.610 = 1.830
medium work	2.8	2.8 x 0.305 = 0.854	2.5	2.5 x 0.854 = 2.135
hard work/light exercise	3.8	3.8 x 0.305 = 1.159	1.5	1.5 x 1.159 = 1.739
moderate exercise	5.0	5.0 x 0.305 = 1.525	0.5	0.5 x 1.525 = 0.763
heavy exercise	6.7	6.7 x 0.305 = 2.043	0.5	0.5 x 2.043 = 1.022
TOTAL			**24**	**13.105**

Overall Physical Activity Level = total energy expenditure ÷ BMR = 13.105 ÷ 7.32 = 1.79

Exercise: Construct an activity diary for yourself, like those shown in tables 5 and 6, and taking your BMR from Table 1 or 2 (depending on whether you wish to calculate in calories or Joules). What is your PAL? What would be the effect of walking fairly briskly for 30 minutes a day?

The energy cost of physical activity increases more sharply with body weight than does BMR, because of the higher energy cost of moving a heavier body. Tables 7 and 8 show average energy requirements of people with different body weights, and different Physical Activity Levels.

Table 7 Average energy requirements at different levels of physical activity, kcal/day

		PAL	body weight (kg)				
			50	60	70	80	90
age 10–17	males	1.2	1829	2039	2249	2458	2668
		1.4	2134	2379	2623	2868	3113
		1.6	2439	2718	2998	3278	3558
		1.8	2743	3058	3373	3688	4002
		2.0	3048	3398	3748	4097	4447
	females	1.2	1625	1772	1918	2064	2210
		1.4	1896	2067	2237	2408	2579
		1.6	2167	2362	2557	2752	2947
		1.8	2438	2657	2877	3096	3315
		2.0	2709	2953	3196	3440	3684
age 18–29	males	1.2	1731	1915	2098	2282	2465
		1.4	2020	2234	2448	2662	2876
		1.6	2309	2553	2798	3043	3287
		1.8	2597	2872	3148	3423	3698
		2.0	2886	3192	3497	3803	4109
	females	1.2	1478	1654	1830	2007	2183
		1.4	1724	1930	2135	2341	2547
		1.6	1970	2205	2441	2676	2911
		1.8	2217	2481	2746	3010	3274
		2.0	2463	2757	3051	3344	3638
age 30–59	males	1.2	1747	1886	2025	2164	2303
		1.4	2038	2201	2363	2525	2687
		1.6	2330	2515	2700	2886	3071
		1.8	2621	2829	3038	3247	3455
		2.0	2912	3144	3376	3607	3839
	females	1.2	1516	1621	1725	1830	1934
		1.4	1769	1891	2013	2134	2256
		1.6	2022	2161	2300	2439	2578
		1.8	2275	2431	2588	2744	2901
		2.0	2527	2701	2875	3049	3223
over 60	males	1.2	1395	1557	1719	1881	2043
		1.4	1627	1816	2005	2194	2383
		1.6	1860	2075	2291	2507	2723
		1.8	2092	2335	2578	2821	3064
		2.0	2324	2594	2864	3134	3404
	females	1.2	1343	1469	1595	1721	1846
		1.4	1567	1714	1861	2007	2154
		1.6	1791	1959	2126	2294	2462
		1.8	2015	2203	2392	2581	2770
		2.0	2238	2448	2658	2868	3077

Table 8 Average energy requirements at different levels of physical activity, MJ/day

		PAL	body weight (kg)				
			50	60	70	80	90
age 10–17	males	1.2	7.66	8.53	9.41	10.29	11.17
		1.4	8.93	9.96	10.98	12.01	13.03
		1.6	10.21	11.38	12.55	13.72	14.89
		1.8	11.48	12.80	14.12	15.44	16.75
		2.0	12.76	14.22	15.69	17.15	18.62
	females	1.2	6.80	7.42	8.03	8.64	9.25
		1.4	7.94	8.65	9.37	10.08	10.79
		1.6	9.07	9.89	10.70	11.52	12.34
		1.8	10.21	11.12	12.04	12.96	13.88
		2.0	11.34	12.36	13.38	14.40	15.42
age 18–29	males	1.2	7.25	8.02	8.78	9.55	10.32
		1.4	8.46	9.35	10.25	11.14	12.04
		1.6	9.66	10.69	11.71	12.74	13.76
		1.8	10.87	12.02	13.18	14.33	15.48
		2.0	12.08	13.36	14.64	15.92	17.20
	females	1.2	6.19	6.92	7.66	8.40	9.14
		1.4	7.22	8.08	8.94	9.80	10.66
		1.6	8.25	9.23	10.22	11.20	12.18
		1.8	9.28	10.39	11.49	12.60	13.71
		2.0	10.31	11.54	12.77	14.00	15.23
age 30–59	males	1.2	7.31	7.90	8.48	9.06	9.64
		1.4	8.53	9.21	9.89	10.57	11.25
		1.6	9.75	10.53	11.30	12.08	12.86
		1.8	10.97	11.84	12.72	13.59	14.46
		2.0	12.19	13.16	14.13	15.10	16.07
	females	1.2	6.35	6.78	7.22	7.66	8.10
		1.4	7.41	7.92	8.43	8.93	9.44
		1.6	8.46	9.05	9.63	10.21	10.79
		1.8	9.52	10.18	10.83	11.49	12.14
		2.0	10.58	11.31	12.04	12.76	13.49
over 60	males	1.2	5.84	6.52	7.19	7.87	8.55
		1.4	6.81	7.60	8.39	9.18	9.98
		1.6	7.78	8.69	9.59	10.50	11.40
		1.8	8.76	9.77	10.79	11.81	12.83
		2.0	9.73	10.86	11.99	13.12	14.25
	females	1.2	5.62	6.15	6.68	7.20	7.73
		1.4	6.56	7.17	7.79	8.40	9.02
		1.6	7.50	8.20	8.90	9.60	10.31
		1.8	8.43	9.22	10.01	10.80	11.59
		2.0	9.37	10.25	11.13	12.00	12.88

Food as an energy source

There are four main types of energy source in foods: carbohydrates, fats, protein and alcohol. Collectively these are sometimes known as metabolic fuels. Table 9 shows the energy yields of these four metabolic fuels. In addition there is a small amount of energy from the acids in fruits (and vinegar), averaging about 2 kcal/g (8 kJ/g).

Table 10 shows the percentage of energy that comes from each of the metabolic fuels in average British diets, and the percentage from each that is considered desirable for health based on numerous studies of diet and health in many countries over the last 50 years. What is required is a reduction in the percentage of energy from fat, by replacing it with carbohydrate.

Table 9 The energy yields of metabolic fuels

	kcal/g	kJ/g
protein	4	17
carbohydrate	4	16
fat	9	37
alcohol	7	29
organic acids	2	8

Table 10 Average and desirable percentage of energy intake from different metabolic fuels

	average	desirable
fat	40	30
carbohydrate	43	53
protein	14	14
alcohol	3	(3)

The apparent discrepancy between 4 kcal/g for both carbohydrate and protein, and 16 and 17 kJ/g respectively, is due to rounding off; these are the officially established values for the energy yields. The figure of 7 kcal/g (29 kJ/g) for alcohol is for pure alcohol; see Table 24 for the alcohol content of beverages.

Table 11 shows how to calculate the percentage of energy from each metabolic fuel in a food; you can use exactly the same type of calculation for a whole meal, or a complete day's meals.

Exercise: *Calculate how many grams of each of carbohydrate, fat and protein you would need to eat each day to meet your energy requirement (either calculated from an activity diary or from the figures in Table 7 or 8) in order to achieve the desirable percentage of energy from each source.*

Table 11 Specimen calculation of the percentage of energy from fat, carbohydrate and protein in a food. The example is milk chocolate (food number 215 in Table 22).

	g/100g food	kcal/g	∴ kcal	% total energy
fat	30.3	9	9 x 30.3 = 272	(272 ÷ 544) x 100 = 50.0
carbohydrate	59.4	4	4 x 59.4 = 238	(238 ÷ 544) x 100 = 43.75
protein	8.4	4	4 x 8.4 = 34	(34 ÷ 544) x 100 = 6.25
TOTAL			**544**	

Carbohydrates

The simplest carbohydrates are the **sugars**, which in turn can be divided into four groups:

- Monosaccharides are single sugar units. Those that occur in foods are mainly glucose, galactose and fructose;

- Sugar alcohols are chemically modified monosaccharides that occur in some fruits naturally, and are widely used in foods designed to be suitable for use by diabetics or those who wish to reduce their energy intake. They are only slowly absorbed, and are poorly metabolized, so they have a lower energy yield than sugars, but are almost as sweet. The main sugar alcohol in foods is sorbitol;

- Disaccharides consist of two linked monosaccharide units. The main disaccharides in foods are:

  - sucrose (cane or beet sugar, consisting of glucose plus fructose);

  - lactose (milk sugar, consisting of galactose plus glucose)

  - trehalose, maltose (malt sugar) and isomaltose, all of which consist of two glucose units linked in different ways).

- Oligosaccharides consist of between 3 to 10 monosaccharide units. They are generally not digested by human enzymes, and form part of the non-starch polysaccharide or dietary fibre of the diet (see page 12).

Sugars, and especially sucrose, which is the main sugar in the diet, are associated with the development of dental decay, and possibly also with obesity, diabetes, and heart disease. It has become conventional to divide sugars in foods into three groups that are quite different from the chemical classification described above:

- **Intrinsic sugars** are found in fruits and vegetables, contained within plant cell walls. They are not considered to pose any hazard for dental decay or other diseases. It is not proposed that average intakes of intrinsic sugars should be reduced, since, for various reasons it is considered desirable that intakes of fruit and vegetables should increase;

- **Extrinsic sugars** are found free in solution in foods, e.g. in jams, sweets, lemonade, fruit juice and in foods to which sugar has been added, such as cakes, etc. It is extrinsic sugars that promote dental decay, and it is considered desirable that average intakes of extrinsic sugars (mainly sucrose) should be reduced.

- The sugar in milk, lactose, is an extrinsic sugar, since it is free in solution. However, lactose is not associated with dental decay. Milk is an important source of protein, calcium and vitamin B_2, and it is not desirable that people should reduce their intake of milk. Therefore, we sometimes subdivide the extrinsic sugars into **milk sugar** and **non-milk extrinsic sugars**.

The major carbohydrate in the diet is **starch**, which is a **polysaccharide** – a large polymer of glucose units – many hundreds or thousands in each molecule. There are two main types of starch – polymers that consist of a single chain of glucose units, and polymers that are branched. Different foods provide different proportions of these two types of starch, as well as a number of smaller glucose polymers, collectively known as dextrins. You will sometimes see starches referred to as **complex carbohydrates**.

Most starch is digested in the small intestine to glucose, maltose and isomaltose, which are then absorbed. However, a proportion of dietary starch is resistant to digestion (and therefore is sometimes known as **resistant starch**); it enters the large intestine, and may be fermented by the gut bacteria to a limited extent. The proportion of starch that is resistant varies widely from one food to another, and also with the type of cooking, whether cooked food has been allowed to cool, been reheated, etc. Therefore there is no easy way of knowing how much starch in a food is readily digested and how much is resistant. Experimentally, the proportion of resistant starch can be measured by measuring the **glycaemic index** of a food – the increase in blood glucose after eating the food compared with the increase after eating an equivalent amount of glucose.

Table 12 Average and desirable percentage of energy intake from different carbohydrates

	average	desirable
total carbohydrate	43	53
starch	24	48
total sugars	19	15
sucrose	14	10
lactose	3	3
glucose	2	2

Table 12 shows the average and desirable percentages of energy intake from different types of carbohydrate.

Foods from plant sources also contain a considerable variety of other complex carbohydrates, which are not digested, and therefore have no nutritional value as metabolic fuels. Collectively these are known as **non-starch polysaccharides**, since they are polysaccharides, but not starch. They may be polymers of glucose linked in a different way from the linkages in starch (e.g. cellulose), or they may contain a variety of other monosaccharide units as well. Non-starch polysaccharides are measured in foods by specific chemical measurement of their constituent monosaccharide units.

An older way of measuring the non-digestible remnants of plant cell walls was less specific, and included a number of compounds that are not chemically polysaccharides. What is measured by this method is known as **dietary fibre** – a somewhat misleading term, since, while some of the compounds measured may indeed be fibrous, others are small oligosaccharides or gelatinous gums.

Although non-starch polysaccharides (or dietary fibre) have no nutritional value, apart from the small amount of energy referred to below, they are important in the diet for a number of reasons:

- They provide bulk in the diet, reduce pressure in the gut, and so help to avoid hernia, varicose veins and diverticular disease of the colon;

- Soluble non-starch polysaccharides (**soluble fibre**) increase the viscosity of the gut contents, and so slow the absorption of the products of

digestion. This may be valuable in the prevention or treatment of diabetes;

- They bind the bile salts, which are formed from cholesterol, so that they are not reabsorbed, but are lost in the faeces. This means that more cholesterol must be used for synthesis of bile salts, and diets high in non-starch polysaccharides are useful as a means of lowering blood cholesterol levels (see page 16)

- They bind a number of compounds in foods that are potentially able to cause cancer, so that they cannot be absorbed;

- A small (and variable) proportion of non-starch polysaccharide, and also of resistant starch, is fermented by bacteria in the large intestine to produce short-chain fatty acids which can be absorbed and used as a source of energy. Some of the products of this bacterial action are protective against cancer of the colon.

There is no agreement within the European Union on whether figures for non-starch polysaccharides or for dietary fibre should be used for food labelling. Therefore, when the information is available, we have included figures for both in Table 22. Because the two methods of analysis measure different things, there is no way of calculating non-starch polysaccharide from dietary fibre, or *vice versa*.

Fat

The fat in our diet is present in various forms: oils and fats added during food preparation, or spread on bread, obvious fat that we can see in meat, and the hidden fat such as that in even the lean parts of meat. There are even small amounts of fat in cereals. All of these are chemically the same, by far the greatest part being triglycerides (also called triacylglycerols), with small amounts of phospholipids and cholesterol. Collectively they are known as **lipids**. The difference between oils and fats is simply that oils are liquid at room temperature, while fats are solid.

Triglycerides are nutritionally the most important; the body can make as much phospholipid and cholesterol as it needs from triglycerides and other components of the diet. Indeed, there is no requirement for fat in the diet, apart from small amounts of two fatty acids which cannot be synthesized in the body. Nevertheless, fat is important in the diet for a number of reasons:

- Fat is a concentrated energy source compared with carbohydrate or protein (see Table 9), and on a very low fat diet it is difficult to eat a large enough amount of food to meet energy needs;

- Fat lubricates food, making chewing and swallowing easier;

- Much of the flavour of many foods is carried in the fat;

- Four of the vitamins (vitamins A, D, E, and K) are fat-soluble, and are only absorbed dissolved in fat.

Triglycerides consist of glycerol attached to three molecules of fatty acid. Fatty acids are chains of carbon atoms from 4 to 22 carbons in length, with an acidic group at one end. It is the acidic group that is attached (esterified) to glycerol. The length of the carbon chains of the fatty acids is one of the factors that determines whether a triglyceride is an oil or a solid fat – triglycerides with longer chain fatty acids melt at a higher temperature. The other factor that determines the melting point of a fat is the degree of saturation of the fatty acids – the more saturated the fatty acids, the higher the melting point of the triglyceride.

In a **saturated** fatty acid, all of the carbon atoms in the chain carry their full quota of hydrogen bonds, and the carbon atoms are linked by single bonds, as shown in Figure 1, which is the structure of the 18-carbon saturated fatty acid, stearic acid.

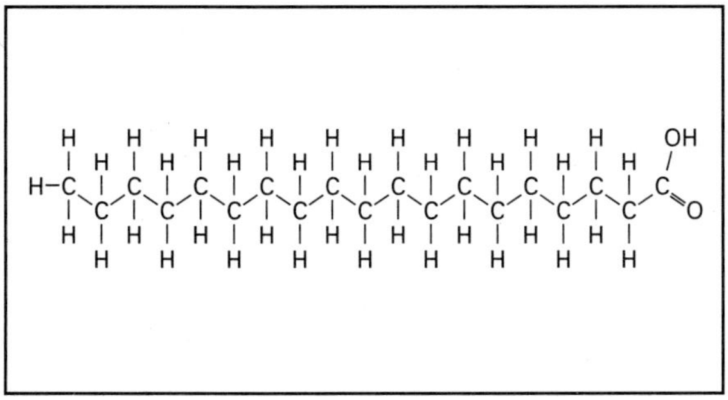

If one hydrogen atom is missing from each of two adjacent carbon atoms, then they are linked by a double bond instead of a single bond. This is a **mono-unsaturated** fatty acid; Figure 2 shows the structure of the 18-carbon mono-unsaturated fatty acid, oleic acid.

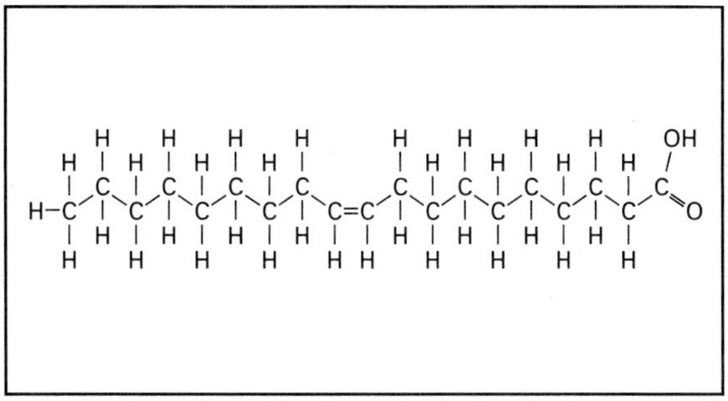

Figure 2 A mono-unsaturated fatty acid

If there are two or more double bonds between pairs of carbon atoms, then the fatty acid is polyunsaturated. Figure 3 shows the structures of two polyunsaturated fatty acids: linoleic acid and α-linolenic acid, which have different numbers of double bonds, and in which the double bonds are in different positions in the chain.

Figure 1 A saturated fatty acid

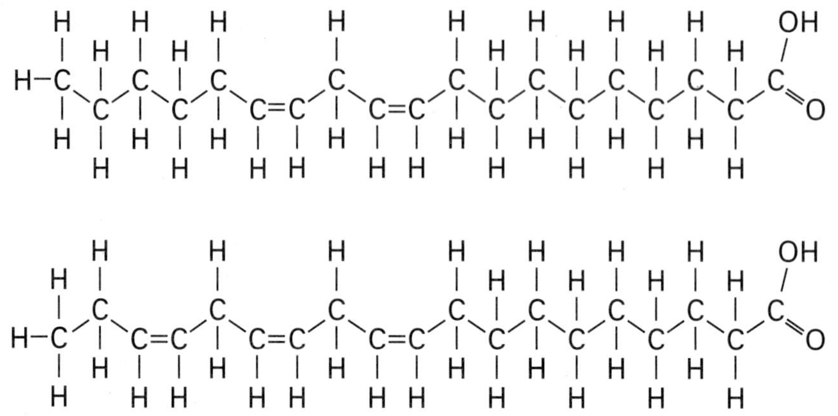

Figure 3 Polyunsaturated fatty acids

Liquid oils can be hardened by hydrogenation – the process of adding hydrogen across some of the double bonds, so converting them to single bonds, and saturating the fatty acid. Hardened vegetable oils and fish oils are used to make margarine, low-fat spreads and cooking fats.

Fats and oils are mixtures of different triglycerides, each of which may contain one, two or three different fatty acids of different chain length and degree of saturation. Usually one kind of fatty acid predominates, so the resultant mixture may be hard (e.g. lard, dripping or coconut fat), soft (e.g. butter or margarine) or liquid (e.g. olive oil, or sunflower oil). Mixing different types of oils and fats gives products like cooking fat and shortening, which have the desired degree of hardness and other properties. Fish oils consist largely of very long chain fatty acids (20–22 carbons), with 4, 5 or 6 double bonds.

Strictly speaking, it is the fatty acids that are saturated or unsaturated, but it is common to refer to saturated, mono-unsaturated and polyunsaturated fats, meaning the type of fatty acid that predominates in the fat.

The naming of fatty acids

All of the fatty acids have formal chemical names, and many of them also have common (trivial) names, which often reflect the oil they were first isolated from – e.g. palmitic and palmitoleic acids from palm oil, oleic acid from olive oil, linoleic and linolenic acids from linseed oil.

There is also a simple shorthand way of naming fatty acids, by stating the number of carbon atoms, followed by a colon and the number of double bonds:

- ■ stearic acid (see Figure 1) has 18 carbon atoms and no double bonds. Its shorthand code is C18:0;
- ■ oleic acid (see Figure 2) has 18 carbon atoms and 1 double bond. Its shorthand code is C18:1;
- ■ linoleic acid (see Figure 3) has 18 carbon atoms and 2 double bonds. Its shorthand code is C18:2;
- ■ α-linolenic acid (see Figure 3) has 18 carbon atoms and 3 double bonds. Its shorthand code is C18:3.

Unsaturated fatty acids can be divided into three groups, depending on the position of the first double bond, counted from the end *furthest* from the acid group. In chemical naming of compounds, the carbon to which the functional group (in fatty acids this is the acid group) is attached is known as the α-carbon, and the carbon atom furthest away is the ω-carbon (alpha, α, is the first letter of the Greek alphabet, and omega, ω, the last). This is shown in the shorthand code by adding ω and the number of the carbon atom from which the first double bond starts(3, 6, or 9):

- in oleic acid the first double bond is at carbon 9 from the end, so its full shorthand code is C18:1 ω9;

- in linoleic acid the first double bond is at carbon 6 from the end, so its full shorthand code is C18:2 ω6

- in α-linolenic acid the first double bond is at carbon 3 from the end, so its full shorthand code is C18:3 ω3

The position of the first double bond from the end of the fatty acid is important; we can *unsaturate* fatty acids in the body to form the ω9 series from saturated fatty acids (e.g. to form oleic acid from stearic acid), and can add further double bonds between the acid group and a double bond, but we cannot add double bonds between the ω-carbon and an existing double bond to make ω3 or ω6 fatty acids. This means that there is a requirement for both ω3 and ω6 fatty acids in the diet: linoleic and α-linolenic acids are sometimes called the **essential fatty acids** because they must be provided in the diet.

The main fatty acids found in foods are shown in Table 13. Note that all of the nutritionally important, and indeed nearly all of the naturally occurring, fatty acids, have an even number of carbon atoms.

Table 13 The naming of fatty acids

	C atoms	double bonds number	first	shorthand
saturated				
butyric	4	0	–	C4:0
caproic	6	0	–	C6:0
caprylic	8	0	–	C8:0
capric	10	0	–	C10:0
lauric	12	0	–	C12:0
myristic	14	0	–	C14:0
palmitic	16	0	–	C16:0
stearic	18	0	–	C18:0
arachidic	20	0	–	C20:0
behenic	22	0	–	C22:0
lignoceric	24	0	–	C24:0
mono-unsaturated				
palmitoleic	16	1	6	C16:1 ω6
oleic	18	1	9	C18:1 ω9
polyunsaturated				
linoleic	18	2	6	C18:2 ω6
α-linolenic	18	3	3	C18:3 ω3
γ-linolenic	18	3	6	C18:3 ω6
arachidonic	20	4	6	C20:4 ω6
eicosapentaenoic	20	5	3	C20:5 ω3
docosatetraenoic	22	4	6	C22:4 ω6
docosapentaenoic	22	5	3	C22:5 ω3
docosapentaenoic	22	5	6	C22:5 ω6
docosahexaenoic	22	6	3	C22:6 ω3

Cis- and trans-fatty acids

There is a final complication in the chemistry of fatty acids that is also important in nutrition. When carbon atoms in a chain are joined by single bonds, there is free rotation about each bond. However, a double bond does not allow rotation. This means that there are two possible arrangements of the chain around a double bond, as shown in Figure 4:

- The chain may continue on the same side of the double bond (above it in this diagram). This is known as the *cis*-conformation;

- The chain may continue on the opposite side of the double bond. This is known as the *trans*-conformation.

15

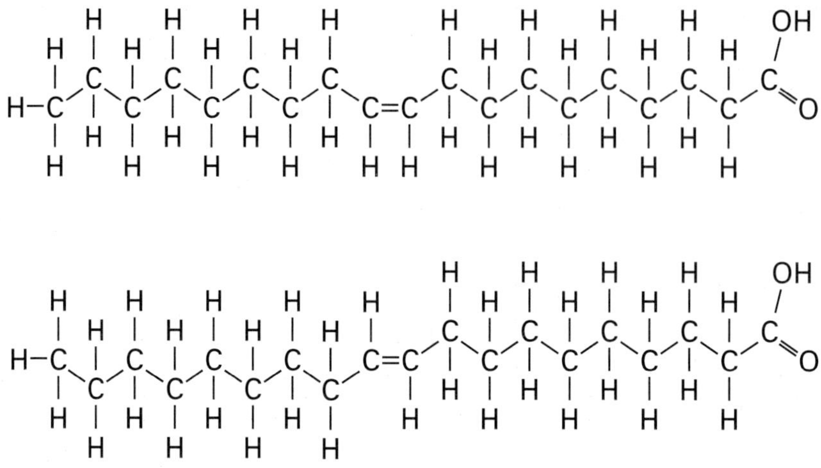

Figure 4 *Cis-* and *trans-* forms of unsaturated fatty acid

Although *cis-* and *trans-* forms of the fatty acids behave the same chemically, the molecules have very different shapes, and they behave differently in the body. Most of the naturally occurring unsaturated fatty acids have the *cis*-conformation. Small amounts of *trans*-fatty acids are found in foods, either naturally occurring (e.g. in beef and lamb fat and in milk), or as a result of re-arrangement of molecules during hydrogenation of unsaturated oils to harden them for margarine manufacture.

As described on page 15 unsaturated fatty acids have beneficial effects in the body. This is only true of the *cis*-forms; by contrast, *trans*-unsaturated fatty acids have no beneficial effects, and indeed may have adverse effects.

Cholesterol

Chemically, cholesterol is a sterol, and is completely different from the triglycerides. Furthermore, it is not metabolized to any significant extent as a metabolic fuel, but is used in the structure of cell membranes, in the synthesis of steroid hormones, and in the formation of the bile salts. Cholesterol does not have to be provided in the diet, since it can be synthesized in the body.

A high blood concentration of cholesterol is a major factor in heart disease, and both the dietary intake of cholesterol and the types of fatty acids in the diet affect the blood concentration:

- Dietary cholesterol is relatively unimportant, since it increases blood cholesterol by a factor related to the square root of intake;

- Saturated fatty acids are much more important, since they increase blood cholesterol by a factor related to 2 x the dietary intake;

- Mono-unsaturated and polyunsaturated fatty acids are beneficial, since they decrease blood cholesterol by a factor related to 0.5 x the dietary intake.

This means that we must consider not just the total amount of fat in the diet, but also the different types of fatty acids. Table 14 shows the average and desirable percentage of energy from different types of fat.

Table 14 Average and desirable percentage of energy from different types of fat

	average	desirable
total fat	37	30
saturated fat	17	10
mono-unsaturated fat	12	12
polyunsaturated fat	6	6
trans-isomers	2	2

In general, fats from animal sources (the fat in meat, dripping, lard, and dairy fats) are relatively high in saturated fatty acids, while oils from plant sources and fish are relatively high in mono- and polyunsaturated fatty acids. Cholesterol is found only in fats from animal sources. This means that in order to achieve the desirable levels of fat intake shown in Table 14, we should be reducing our intake of fats from animal sources and increasing the proportion of fat that comes from vegetable sources and fish.

The oils from fish such as herring, mackerel, sardines, salmon and trout (and also cod and halibut liver oils) are especially rich in long-chain ω3 polyunsaturated fatty acids. These confer a further benefit to health – not only do they reduce blood cholesterol, like other unsaturated fatty acids, but they also reduce the risk of blood clots forming in the arteries and veins.

Protein

The protein content of foods is usually measured by analysing for total nitrogen (by the Kjeldahl method), since protein is the main nitrogen-containing component of the diet (although there is also some non-protein nitrogen in foods). On average, proteins contain 16% nitrogen (N), and therefore for most foods (and certainly for mixed diets) we calculate protein as 100/16 x mass of N(g) = 6.25 x mass of N(g).

The precise factors used for some foods differ because of the differences in the mixture of amino acids that make up different proteins:

- for legumes, protein = 5.3 x N(g);
- for cereals, protein = 5.7 x N(g);
- for meat, protein = 6.25 x N(g);
- for milk, protein = 6.38 x N(g).

There is an obvious need for protein in the diet of a child, or a pregnant woman, to provide for the increase in the total amount of protein in the body. However, adults, who are not growing, also require dietary protein, because there is continual breakdown and replacement of all the proteins in the body.

As long as the intake of protein is adequate to replace the losses, any that is surplus to requirements is metabolized, and the nitrogen part is excreted from the body as a variety of nitrogen-containing compounds. If the intake is not adequate to meet requirements, then nitrogenous compounds excreted as a result of body protein breakdown will not be replaced.

We can measure the total intake and excretion of nitrogen-containing compounds (again by the Kjeldahl method). The difference between intake and excretion is **nitrogen balance**:

- If intake and excretion of nitrogen-containing compounds are equal, then the subject is in nitrogen balance or equilibrium. This is the normal state in an adult, and means that the intake is equal to, or greater than, requirements.

- If the intake is greater than the excretion of nitrogen-containing compounds, then the subject is in **positive nitrogen balance**. This means that there is an increase in the total amount of nitrogen (i.e. the total amount of protein) in the body. This is normal in growth and pregnancy, and also when recovering from any body protein loss.

- If the intake is less than the excretion of nitrogen-containing compounds, then the subject is in **negative nitrogen balance**. This means that there is a nett loss of nitrogen (i.e. protein) from the body. This is never normal. Negative nitrogen balance occurs in two conditions:

  a) in response to major injury, burns, and infection;

  b) when the intake of protein is less than is required.

This means that we can use measurement of nitrogen balance to estimate protein requirements by feeding people on varying levels of protein intake until we find the intake at which they can just maintain nitrogen balance.

The average requirement for adults is 0.6 g of protein/kg body weight; adding a factor to allow for individual variation leads to a Reference Nutrient Intake of 0.75 g protein/kg body weight. Reference Nutrient Intakes for protein are shown in Table 15 on page 18.

Table 15 Reference Nutrient Intakes for protein

	age	mg/kg body weight	g/day
	0–3m	–	12.5
	3–6 m	1649	12.7
	6–9 m	1557	13.7
	9–12 m	1536	13.7
	1–3 y	1160	14.5
	4–6 y	1106	19.7
	7–10 y	1000	28.3
males	11–14 y	950	42.1
	15–18 y	900	55.2
	19–24 y	750	55.5
	25–50 y	750	55.5
	over 51	750	53.3
females	11–14 y	950	41.2
	15–18 y	900	45.0
	19–24 y	750	45.0
	25–50 y	750	45.0
	over 51	750	46.5
	pregnant	–	+ 6
	lactating 1–6 m	–	+ 11
	lactating over 6 m	–	+ 8

An alternative way of expressing protein requirements is to express protein as a percentage of energy intake (see Table 11 for an example of how to calculate this). On this basis, the Reference Nutrient Intake is 7.5% of energy. The average intake of protein in Britain is 14% of energy intake.

Exercise: Starchy foods such as potatoes, pasta, rice and bread are normally considered to be sources of carbohydrate, and people often ignore their protein. From the figures in Table 22, calculate the percentage of energy provided by protein in these foods.

B) The need for food: vitamins and minerals

Vitamins are small organic (i.e. carbon-containing) compounds that are required for the maintenance of normal body functions. They cannot be synthesized in the body, so must be provided in the diet. Unlike protein and the essential fatty acids, they are required in very small amounts – mg or µg/day. Deficiency of a vitamin leads to a relatively specific deficiency disease which is cured by restoring the vitamin to the diet. Table 16 shows the functions of, and deficiency diseases associated with, the vitamins.

Although all of the vitamins are essential for health, not all of them are nutritionally important, in that they are so widespread in foods that deficiency is more or less completely unknown, except in deliberate experiments to study deficiency and requirements. In Table 22 we show the content of vitamins A, E, B_1, B_2, niacin, B_6, folate, and vitamin C. Very few foods provide significant amounts of vitamin D, and these are listed separately in Table 23.

Table 16 The functions of the vitamins

Vitamin		principal metabolic functions	deficiency disease
A	retinol (β-carotene)	vision – forms the visual pigments in the retina; cell differentiation; β-carotene is an antioxidant	night blindness, xerophthalmia; keratinization of skin.
D	calciferol	maintenance of calcium balance; enhances intestinal absorption of calcium and mobilizes bone mineral	rickets in children = poor mineralization of bone; osteomalacia in adults = bone demineralization
E	tocopherols and tocotrienols	antioxidant, especially in membranes	extremely rare – serious neurological dysfunction
K	phylloquinone and menaquinones	coenzyme in formation of proteins required for blood clotting and some bone proteins	impaired blood clotting, haemorrhagic disease
B_1	thiamin	coenzyme in carbohydrate metabolism; also a rôle in nerve conduction	peripheral nerve damage (beriberi) or central nervous system damage (Wernicke-Korsakoff syndrome)
B_2	riboflavin	coenzyme in many energy yielding reactions	lesions of corner of mouth, lips and tongue, dermatitis
–	niacin (nicotinic acid and nicotinamide)	coenzyme in many energy yielding reactions	pellagra – photosensitive dermatitis, depressive psychosis, fatal
B_6	pyridoxine, pyridoxal and pyridoxamine	coenzyme in amino acid and glycogen metabolism; rôle in steroid hormone action	disorders of amino acid metabolism, convulsions
–	folic acid	coenzyme in transfer of one-carbon fragments	megaloblastic anaemia
B_{12}	cobalamin	coenzyme in transfer of one-carbon fragments and metabolism of folic acid	pernicious anaemia = megaloblastic anaemia with degeneration of the spinal cord.
–	pantothenic acid	coenzyme in fat metabolism	peripheral nerve damage (burning foot syndrome)
H	biotin	coenzyme in carbohydrate and fat metabolism	impaired fat and carbohydrate metabolism, dermatitis
C	ascorbic acid	coenzyme in collagen synthesis; antioxidant; enhances absorption of iron	scurvy – impaired wound healing, loss of dental cement, subcutaneous haemorrhage

Vitamin A

Vitamin A itself (retinol) is found only in foods of animal origin. However, the carotene of vegetable foods is converted to vitamin A in the body. The amount of carotene that is absorbed and converted to retinol in the wall of the intestine varies with the food (e.g. it is better absorbed from a purée of carrots than from whole carrots, and better absorbed when there is fat present). It also varies with the type of carotene in the food.

The total vitamin A content of foods (that present as preformed retinol plus that formed from carotene) is expressed as µg **retinol equivalents**. This is the sum of:

µg preformed retinol

+ 1/6 x µg β-carotene

+ $1/2$ x µg carotene from milk (because carotene from milk is especially well absorbed)

+ 1/12 x µg other carotenes (e.g. α-carotene in red palm oil, cryptoxanthin in yellow maize) because they yield only half as much retinol as does β-carotene.

In Table 22 we have shown the total vitamin A in foods as µg retinol equivalents. We have also shown the carotene content of foods separately, since, as well as being a source of vitamin A, carotene is an anti-oxidant (see page 24).

You will sometimes see vitamin A expressed as i.u. (international units). This dates back to the days before vitamin A could be measured chemically, and had to be measured by its biological activity, using an internationally agreed unit of activity:

- 1 i.u. = 0.3 µg retinol equivalent
- 1 µg retinol equivalent = 3.33 i.u.

Vitamin D

Vitamin D is an exception to the rule that vitamins cannot be synthesized in the body, but must be provided in the diet, since it can be synthesized in the skin on exposure to sunlight. However, in northern latitudes (north of the Midlands in Britain) the amount of sunlight of the correct wavelength for the formation of vitamin D is inadequate to meet requirements, so a dietary source is needed.

Like vitamin A, you will sometimes see vitamin D expressed in international units:

- 1 i.u. = 0.025 µg vitamin D
- 1 µg vitamin D = 40 i.u.

Table 23 on page 86 shows the foods which provide significant amounts of vitamin D.

Vitamin E

Requirements for vitamin E are not well established, and indeed its metabolic function in the body is not completely clear. However, it is an important antioxidant (see page 24).

Eight related compounds, with differing potency, all have vitamin E activity; the most potent, and therefore the main form of the vitamin, is α-tocopherol.

Vitamin E differs from the other vitamins in that the chemically synthesized vitamin does not have the same biological activity as the naturally occurring form. There are 8 different forms of α-tocopherol, with different biological activity; the naturally occurring form (D-α-tocopherol) is the most active, but when it is synthesized chemically the result is a mixture of all the possible forms.

Like vitamins A and D, you will sometimes see vitamin E expressed in international units:

- 1 i.u. = 1 mg synthetic DL-α-tocopherol = 0.67 mg naturally occurring D-α-tocopherol
- 1 mg naturally occurring D-α-tocopherol = 1.49 i.u.

Niacin

Although niacin (nicotinic acid and/or nicotinamide) is a considered to be a vitamin, it can be formed in the body from the amino acid tryptophan. Indeed, average intakes of protein provide more than enough tryptophan to meet niacin requirements. An intake of 60 mg tryptophan is equivalent to 1 mg preformed niacin, and in Table 22 we have given the niacin content of foods as mg niacin equivalents:

1 mg niacin equivalent = mg preformed niacin + 1/60 x mg tryptophan

Minerals

Any inorganic mineral that has a function in the body must obviously be provided in the diet, since it is not possible to interconvert the chemical elements. Table 17 shows the functions of the minerals that are known to be essential.

Table 17 The functions of the minerals

functions	mineral	chemical symbol
structural	calcium	Ca
	magnesium	Mg
	phosphate	PO_4^{3-}
	fluoride	F^-
nerve action	sodium	Na
	potassium	K
enzymes	cobalt	Co
	copper	Cu
	iron	Fe
	molybdenum	Mo
	selenium	Se
	zinc	Zn
hormones or regulation	calcium	Ca
	chromium	Cr
	iodine	I
	magnesium	Mg
	manganese	Mn
	sodium	Na
unknown but essential	nickel	Ni
	silicon	Si
	tin	Sn
	vanadium	V

Although all of these minerals are essential, most are not nutritionally important, since deficiency is extremely unlikely. In Table 22 we have shown information for sodium, calcium, iron and iodine.

Sodium is unusual among the nutrients in that the main concern is about excessive intake rather than deficiency. Average intakes of sodium (mainly from salt added in cooking and at the table) are several times higher than requirements, and sufficiently high to pose a potential risk of developing high blood pressure. The general advice is that we should reduce our intake of sodium.

Requirements and Reference Nutrient Intakes

Requirements for any nutrient are determined by feeding a group of volunteers with a diet that is adequate in all respects except the nutrient under investigation, and measuring sensitive biochemical or other signs of deficiency. The volunteers are then fed increasing amounts of the deficient nutrient until the abnormality is corrected.

Different people, even of the same gender, age and activity, have different requirements for nutrients. The upper graph in Figure 5 shows the distribution of results that would be obtained if requirements for any nutrient were determined in a group of people – a normal distribution. In order to set a figure that is adequate to meet the requirements of more or less everyone, the results are analysed statistically, to find the average (mean) requirement and the standard deviation of the results around the average. The requirements of 95% of the population lie within the range ± 2 x standard deviations around the average. Therefore an intake of 2 x standard deviation above the average requirement is more than adequate to meet the requirements of nearly everyone (97.5% of the population). This is the figure that is known as the **Reference Nutrient Intake (RNI)**, shown in the lower graph in Figure 5. You will also sometimes see the RNI referred to as RDA (Recommended Daily Amount, used in the USA and Canada) or PRI (Population Reference Intake, used in European Union publications).

Figure 5 also shows the **Lower Reference Nutrient Intake (LRNI)**; this is 2 x standard deviation below the average requirement, and therefore lower than the requirement of more or less everyone in the population. Only 2.5% of the population would meet their requirements at this level of intake, so it is a level of intake at or below which it is unlikely that an individual could maintain normal health.

It is important to note that the figures for Reference Nutrient Intakes do not apply to individuals – *the RNI is a level of intake that is greater than the requirements of more or less everyone in the population*. The figures are used to plan food supplies and assess the adequacy of community diets, not the diets of individuals.

The requirements for vitamins E and K, biotin and pantothenic acid are not well established, and there are no RNI for these vitamins. Estimated safe and adequate levels of intake, which are more than adequate to meet requirements, are:

- Vitamin E: men 4 mg/day, women 3 mg/day
- Vitamin K: 1 µg/kg body weight (10 µg/day for infants)
- Pantothenic acid: 3–7 mg/day
- Biotin 10–200 µg/day

RNI for the other vitamins are shown in Table 18, and for minerals in Table 19. Note that there are values of RNI for vitamin D only for infants, elderly people and pregnant and lactating women; for other groups of the population it is assumed that normal sunlight exposure is adequate to meet requirements.

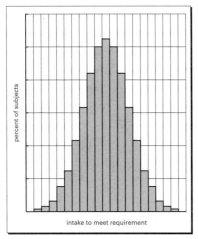

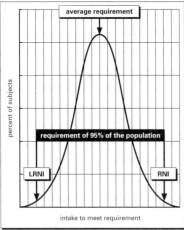

Figure 5 Derivation of Reference Nutrient Intakes

Table 18 Reference Nutrient Intakes of vitamins

	age	A	D	B₁	B₂	niacin	B₆	B₁₂	folate	C
		µg	µg	mg	mg	mg	mg	µg	µg	mg
	0–3 m	350	8.5	0.2	0.4	3	0.2	0.3	50	25
	4–6 m	350	8.5	0.2	0.4	3	0.2	0.3	50	25
	7–9 m	350	7	0.2	0.4	4	0.3	0.4	50	25
	10–12 m	350	7	0.3	0.4	5	0.4	0.4	50	25
	1–3 y	400	7	0.5	0.6	8	0.7	0.5	70	30
	4–6 y	500	–	0.7	0.8	11	0.9	0.8	100	30
	7–10 y	500	–	0.7	1.0	12	1.0	1.0	150	30
males	11–14 y	600	–	0.9	1.2	15	1.2	1.2	200	35
	15–18 y	700	–	1.1	1.3	18	1.5	1.5	200	40
	19–50	700	–	1.0	1.3	17	1.4	1.5	200	40
	over 50	700	10	0.9	1.3	16	1.4	1.5	200	40
females	11–14 y	600	–	0.7	1.1	12	1.0	1.2	200	35
	15–18 y	600	–	0.8	1.1	14	1.2	1.5	200	40
	19–50 y	600	–	0.8	1.1	13	1.2	1.5	200	40
	over 50	600	10	0.8	1.1	12	1.2	1.5	200	40
	pregnant	+100	10	+0.1	+0.3	–	–	–	+100	+10
	lactating	+350	10	+0.1	+0.5	+2	–	+0.5	+60	+30

Table 19 Reference Nutrient Intakes of minerals

	age	Ca	P	Mg	Na	Fe	Zn	Cu	Se	I
		mg	mg	mg	mg	mg	mg	mg	µg	µg
	0–3 m	525	400	55	210	1.7	4.0	0.2	10	50
	4–6 m	525	400	60	280	4.3	4.0	0.3	13	60
	7–9 m	525	400	75	320	7.8	5.0	0.3	10	60
	10–12 m	525	400	80	350	7.8	5.0	0.3	10	60
	1–3 y	350	270	85	500	6.9	5.0	0.4	15	70
	4–6 y	450	350	120	700	6.1	6.5	0.6	20	100
	7–10 y	550	450	200	1200	8.7	7.0	0.7	30	110
males	11–14 y	1000	775	280	1600	11.3	9.0	0.8	45	130
	15–18 y	1000	775	300	1600	11.3	9.5	1.0	70	140
	19–50	700	550	300	1600	8.7	9.5	1.2	75	140
	over 50	700	550	300	1600	8.7	9.5	1.2	75	140
females	11–14 y	800	625	280	1600	14.8	9.0	0.8	45	130
	15–18 y	800	625	300	1600	14.8	7.0	1.0	60	140
	19–50 y	700	550	270	1600	14.8	7.0	1.2	60	140
	over 50	700	550	270	1600	8.7	7.0	1.2	60	140
	pregnant	–	–	–	–	–	–	–	–	–
	lactating	+550	+440	+50	–	–	+6.0	+0.3	+15	–

Higher levels of intake

Reference Nutrient Intakes are calculated from experiments to determine the levels of intake that are required to prevent specific signs of deficiency. It is to be expected that future tables of RNI will concentrate on intakes that promote optimum health, rather than the prevention of deficiency, but as yet there is little or no evidence on which to base such figures. For three nutrients (iron, folic acid and the antioxidant nutrients) there is evidence that levels of intake above RNI, and possibly higher than can be met from a normal mixed diet, may be beneficial.

Iron

Iron deficiency anaemia is relatively common among women of child-bearing age. Up to perhaps 10–15% of women have a loss of iron in the menstrual blood flow that is greater than can be met from even a good diet, because the iron from foods is not well absorbed, and the iron from plant foods is particularly poorly absorbed. Because of this, the European Union tables of Population Reference Intakes (published in 1993) give a very much higher figure for iron for women than for men – and note that this could not be achieved from the diet, but that supplements will be necessary to meet the high iron requirements of at least some women.

Folic acid

Supplements of folic acid of 400 µg/day (on top of a normal intake of about the RNI of 200 µg/day) have been shown to reduce very considerably the risk of a pregnant woman having a child affected by spina bifida or other neural tube defects. This level of intake could not be achieved from foods, so pregnant women are advised to take supplements of folic acid. The problem is that the damage to the developing foetus is done by about day 28 of pregnancy, which is before the woman knows she is pregnant. Therefore the official advice is that all women who are, or who may be about to become, pregnant, should take supplements of 400 µg of folic acid daily.

Because women who *might be about to become pregnant* make up a very considerable proportion of the population, it has been suggested that staple foods (e.g. cereals, bread, etc) should be fortified with folic acid. The problem with this is that widespread fortification of foods with folic acid would lead to some people having an intake that is potentially hazardous. Two groups of the population are involved:

- Elderly people, who have poor absorption of vitamin B_{12}. High intakes of folic acid can mask developing vitamin B_{12} deficiency until there is irreversible nerve damage;

- People with epilepsy that is controlled by medication. High intakes of folic acid can counteract anti-epileptic drugs, and so increase the frequency of attacks.

Antioxidant nutrients

There is a great deal of evidence that heart disease, cancer and possibly some of the diseases of ageing, are due to damage to tissues caused by free radicals. Free radicals are extremely reactive molecules which can cause damage to fatty acids in cell membranes, proteins and DNA, so triggering a variety of diseases. In the body the free radicals that cause most concern are oxygen radicals, which are formed as part of normal metabolism, as well as from smoking, exposure to radiation (including the ultra-violet in sunlight), etc.

A number of nutrients are able to react with oxygen radicals, or with the products of free radical action on fatty acids, and so reduce the damage. Collectively these are known as antioxidant nutrients. The most important are: carotene, vitamin E, vitamin C, and the mineral selenium.

Although people with low intakes of these anti-oxidant nutrients are more at risk of heart disease and some forms of cancer, it is not clear whether or not higher intakes are protective. Indeed, most of the studies in which people have been given supplements of one or other of the antioxidant nutrients have been very disappointing, in that there was no protection, and in some cases the supplements led to more deaths from cancer or heart disease. The problem is that the main sources of anti-oxidant nutrients are fruits and vegetables, and the real evidence is that people with relatively high intakes of fruit and vegetables are less at risk of developing these diseases – there are a great many other potentially protective compounds in plants, as well as the known antioxidant nutrients. Hence the advice is to **consume at least five servings of fruit and vegetables a day**.

Dangers of nutrient toxicity

Although vitamins and minerals are essential in small amounts, this does not mean that larger amounts either provide any benefit or are safe. Several of the minerals are known to be toxic in (relatively modest) excess, as are four vitamins. Other vitamins may also be toxic, although as yet this has not been observed.

Vitamin A provides the most serious cause for concern. As shown in Table 20, there is only a relatively narrow range between the RNI for vitamin A and the level of habitual consumption at which signs of toxicity are observed. For pregnant women the margin of safety is especially narrow – intakes only about 4–5 times greater than the RNI can cause damage to the developing foetus. This is a level of intake that could easily be obtained from foods, and pregnant women have been advised not to eat liver, which is a rich source of vitamin A. There is no problem with high intakes of carotene, since there is only limited conversion of carotene to retinol (see page 20).

Vitamin D is also toxic, especially to young children, at levels of intake that are not very much above RNI. Because of the serious danger of vitamin D poisoning, the enrichment of infant foods with vitamin D has been reduced to such an extent that a small proportion of children are at risk of developing rickets, the vitamin D deficiency disease. Excessive exposure to sunlight does not lead to vitamin D poisoning, because there is a limited ability to synthesize the vitamin in the skin. (But note that excessive exposure to sunlight is a factor in causing skin cancer).

Niacin can cause liver damage at very high levels of intake. This is not a problem of nutritional levels of intake, but only occurs with intakes of about 500 mg/day (compared with an RNI of up to 18 mg/day). These very high levels of niacin are used as a drug to treat patients with very high blood concentrations of cholesterol.

Vitamin B_6 can cause nerve damage at very high levels of intake. Again the problem does not arise with intakes of the vitamin from foods, but only when supplements are taken to treat a variety of conditions such as the premenstrual syndrome. There is clear evidence of nerve damage in people who take more than 500 mg/day (compared with an RNI of up to 1.5 mg/day), and some evidence that intakes above 50 mg/day may also be hazardous.

Table 20 Upper safe limits of habitual vitamin A intake

	upper limit	RNI	ratio
	µg/day	µg/day	upper limit : RNI
infants	900	350	2.6
1–3 years	1800	400	4.5
4–6 years	3000	500	6.0
6–12 years	4500	500	9.0
13–20 years	6000	600–700	8.6–10.0
adult men	9000	700	12.9
adult women	7500	600	12.5
pregnant women	3300	700	4.7

C) The nutrient content of foods

Tables 22 and 23 show the nutrient content of foods. Such tables of food composition are used to assess nutrient and energy intakes, and to plan meals and food supplies. The composition of a food can vary widely, depending on a number of factors:

- The precise variety of plant or animal the food came from;

- The conditions under which the plant was grown or the animal was raised;

- For many vegetables, the freshness. Vitamin C is rapidly lost as vegetables wilt, and indeed frozen vegetables frequently have a higher content of vitamin C than 'fresh' vegetables bought from a shop;

- The way the food has been cooked:

  - Some vitamins and minerals may be lost into the cooking water;

  - Some vitamins are destroyed to a greater or lesser extent by heat;

  - There may be a gain of water when food is steamed, boiled or stewed, so leading to a lower concentration of nutrients per 100 g;

  - There may be a loss of water when food is fried, baked or roasted, so leading to a higher concentration of nutrients per 100 g;

  - Frying obviously increases the fat content of foods very considerably.

In Tables 22 and 23, foods are assumed to be as purchased, or as prepared for cooking, unless the method of cooking is stated. For fried foods, no information about saturated and unsaturated fats is given, since this will depend on the type of oil used for frying.

When very accurate information is required, as in some areas of research, it is necessary to take duplicate portions of all foods eaten and analyse them in the laboratory. This is a very expensive and time-consuming process, and tables of food composition like those in this book are usually used. Because of the natural variation in foods it is never possible to obtain exact figures, and it is likely that there will be an error of as much as ± 10% from the true (analysed) value – and perhaps even higher for some vitamins and minerals. However, this is the best that can be achieved, and indeed, assessing the amount of food eaten may introduce much larger errors. The average serving sizes given in Table 22 should be taken as only a very approximate guide – if you want to be more precise, you should weigh each food eaten.

If you find tables of the nutrient content of foods on Internet and World Wide Web sites, you may well find that they differ from the values in Tables 22 and 23. Most are American tables which sometimes use different methods of analysis from those used in Britain, and sometimes analyse different varieties of foods from those eaten in Britain.

Table 21 shows an example of the calculation of a day's intake from the information in Table 22. Note that at each stage figures are calculated precisely, but then, in the final row they are rounded off, to avoid spurious precision.

Exercise: What are the main sources of protein in this day's meals?

These meals provide a total of 120 g of fat, which is equivalent to 120 x 9 kcal = 1080 kcal. The total energy intake is 2700 kcal, so fat provides 100 x (1080 ÷ 2700) = 40% of energy.

What are the main sources of fat in this diet?

Which foods would you change to reduce fat to 30% of energy?

Table 21 Specimen calculation of the nutrient content of a day's food intake

Food	serving	kcal		protein		fat	
		/100 g	in serving	/100 g	in serving	/100 g	in serving
Breakfast							
cornflakes	20 g	355	0.2 x 355 = 71	7.9	0.2 x 7.9 = 1.58	0.6	0.2 x 0.6 = 0.12
milk	140 ml	66	1.4 x 66 = 92	3.2	1.4 x 3.2 = 4.48	3.9	1.4 x 3.9 = 5.46
sugar	2 tsp = 10 g	394	0.1 x 394 = 39	0	0	0	0
bread	2 slices = 70 g	218	0.7 x 218 = 153	8.5	0.7 x 8.5 = 5.95	2.0	0.7 x 2.0 = 1.40
butter	15 g	737	0.15 x 737 = 111	0.5	0.15 x 0.5 = 0.08	81.7	0.15 x 81.7 = 12.25
coffee	1 cup = 150 ml	0	0	0	0	0	0
milk	20 ml	66	0.2 x 66 = 13	3.2	0.2 x 3.2 = 0.64	3.9	0.2 x 3.9 = 0.78
sugar	2 tsp = 10 g	394	0.1 x 394 = 39	0	0	0	0
Total: Breakfast			**479**		**12.73**		**20.01**
Mid-morning							
bread roll	50 g	280	0.5 x 280 = 140	10.9	0.5 x 10.9 = 5.45	2.3	0.5 x 2.3 = 1.15
cheddar cheese	40 g	412	0.4 x 412 = 165	25.5	0.4 x 25.5 = 10.2	34.4	0.4 x 34.4 = 13.76
butter	15 g	737	0.15 x 737 = 111	0.5	0.15 x 0.5 = 0.08	81.7	0.15 x 81.7 = 12.25
tea	cup = 150 ml	0	0	0	0	0	0
milk	20 ml	66	0.2 x 66 = 13	3.2	0.2 x 3.2 = 0.64	3.9	0.2 x 3.9 = 0.78
sugar	2 tsp = 10 g	394	0.1 x 394 = 39	0	0	0	0
Total: Mid-morning			**468**		**16.37**		**27.94**
Lunch							
fried cod	180 g	199	1.8 x 199 = 358	19.6	1.8 x 19.6 = 35.28	10.3	1.8 x 10.3 = 18.54
chips	165 g	189	1.65 x 189 = 312	3.9	1.65 x 3.9 = 6.44	6.7	1.65 x 6.7 = 11.06
peas	70 g	79	0.7 x 79 = 55	6.7	0.7 x 6.7 = 4.69	1.6	0.7 x 1.6 = 1.12
lemonade	330 ml	21	3.3 x 21 = 102	0	0	0	0
Total: Lunch			**827**		**46.41**		**30.72**
Evening meal							
avocado	half = 75 g	134	0.75 x 134 = 101	1.3	0.75 x 1.3 = 0.98	13.8	0.75 x 13.8 = 10.35
roast beef	100 g	192	1 x 192 = 192	27.6	1 x 27.6 = 27.6	9.1	1 x 9.1 = 9.1
roast potatoes	200 g	149	2 x 149 = 298	2.9	2 x 2.9 = 5.8	4.5	2 x 4.5 = 9.0
Yorkshire pudding	80 g	208	0.8 x 208 = 166	6.6	0.8 x 6.6 = 5.28	9.9	0.8 x 9.9 = 7.92
runner beans	90 g	18	0.9 x 18 = 16	1.2	0.9 x 1.2 = 1.08	0.5	0.9 x 0.5 = 0.45
fruit cocktail	115 g	57	1.15 x 57 = 66	0.4	1.15 x 0.4 = 0.46	0	0
ice cream	60 g	194	0.6 x 194 = 116	3.6	0.6 x 3.6 = 2.16	9.8	0.6 x 9.8 = 5.88
Total: Evening meal			**955**		**43.36**		**42.7**
Total for day			**2699**		**118.87**		**121.37**
Rounded off			**2700**		**120**		**120**

Note that 120 g of fat = 120 x 9 = 1080 kcal; in this day's food fat provides 100 x (1080 ÷ 2700) = 40% of energy

How to use Table 22

This table shows the nutrient content as g (or mg or µg) per 100g (or per 100 ml for liquids) of the food; the exception is the data for saturated, mono-unsaturated and polyunsaturated fats, which are shown as percentage of the total fat. The first column of numbers shows the size of an average serving of the food (in g or ml) where this is appropriate. This is to guide and help you if you have not been able to the weigh foods you have eaten.

Carbohydrates include substances that are either not metabolized, or are incompletely metabolized, so that the sum of starch plus sugars may be less than the total carbohydrate.

As explained on page 20, vitamin A is shown as µg retinol equivalents (the sum of preformed vitamin A plus that formed from carotene), and niacin is shown as mg niacin equivalents (the sum of preformed niacin plus that formed from tryptophan).

A value of 0 indicates that the food provides only a negligible amount of the nutrient in question, if any at all. A dash (–) indicates that no information is available, or, in the case of fried foods, that the information on saturated and unsaturated fats depends on the type of oil used for frying.

There are blank lines at the end of Table 22 for you to add in the composition of dishes that you have prepared yourself – you do this by weighing each of the ingredients you use, and looking up the composition of each ingredient in Table 22.

Table 22 Nutrient content of foods per 100 g

per 100 g		average serving	water	energy	energy	protein	carbohydrates	starch	sugars	fat	saturated	mono-unsaturated	poly-unsaturated	cholesterol
		g	g	kcal	kJ	g	g	g	g	g	%	%	%	mg
1 advocaat		25	47.6	272	1139	4.7	28.4	0.0	28.4	6.3	32.8	51.7	15.5	242
2 All-Bran breakfast cereal		30	3.0	252	1055	15.1	43.0	27.6	15.4	3.4	24.0	16.0	60.0	0
3 almonds, shelled	20 kernels	20	4.2	612	2562	21.1	6.9	2.7	4.2	55.8	8.8	64.5	26.6	0
4 anchovies, canned in oil	small tin	50	41.6	280	1172	25.2	0.0	0.0	0.0	19.9	–	–	–	–
5 apple juice, unsweetened	1 glass	200	88.0	38	159	0.1	9.9	0.0	9.9	0.1	–	–	–	0
6 apples, cooking		170	63.1	26	109	0.2	6.4	0.0	6.4	0.1	–	–	–	0
7 apples, dessert		110	75.2	42	176	0.4	10.5	0.0	10.5	0.1	–	–	–	0
8 apricots		40	80.2	29	121	0.8	6.6	0.0	6.6	0.1	–	–	–	0
9 apricots, canned in juice		140	87.5	34	142	0.5	8.4	0.0	8.4	0.1	–	–	–	0
10 apricots, canned in syrup		140	80.0	63	264	0.4	16.1	0.0	16.1	0.1	–	–	–	0
11 apricots, dried	4 apricots	30	14.7	188	787	4.8	43.4	0.0	43.4	0.7	–	–	–	0
12 artichoke, globe		50	36.3	8	33	1.2	1.2	0.0	0.6	0.1	–	–	–	0
13 artichoke, Jerusalem		120	80.2	41	172	1.6	10.6	0.0	1.6	0.1	–	–	–	0
14 asparagus	5 spears	125	91.5	26	109	3.4	1.4	0.0	1.4	0.8	16.7	33.3	50.0	0
15 aubergine	1/2 aubergine	130	92.9	15	63	0.9	2.2	0.2	2.0	0.4	–	–	–	0
16 avocado	1/2 fruit	75	51.5	134	561	1.3	1.3	0.0	0.4	13.8	22.1	65.6	12.2	0
17 babaco	1 slice	140	93.9	17	71	1.1	3.1	0.0	3.1	0.1	–	–	–	0
18 bacon collar joint, boiled		100	60.8	191	800	26.0	0.0	0.0	0.0	9.7	40.9	47.7	11.4	36
19 bacon rasher, back grilled	2 rashers	50	36.0	405	1695	25.3	0.0	0.0	0.0	33.8	41.3	47.8	10.9	125
20 bacon rasher, middle, grilled	2 rashers	80	35.2	416	1741	24.9	0.0	0.0	0.0	35.1	41.3	47.6	11.1	130
21 bacon rasher, streaky, grilled	2 rashers	40	34.6	422	1766	24.5	0.0	0.0	0.0	36.0	41.2	47.7	11.1	133
22 bacon, gammon joint, boiled		100	62.7	167	699	29.4	0.0	0.0	0.0	5.5	42.0	48.0	10.0	20
23 bacon, gammon steak, grilled		170	57.0	172	720	31.4	0.0	0.0	0.0	5.2	41.3	47.8	10.9	19
24 banana	1 fruit	100	49.6	62	260	0.8	15.3	1.5	13.8	0.2	–	–	–	0
25 banana, green (matoki)	1 fruit	200	74.1	91	381	1.3	22.3	21.7	0.6	0.2	–	–	–	0
26 barbecue sauce	1 portion pack	20	80.9	75	314	1.8	12.2	–	–	1.8	16.7	44.4	38.9	0
27 Barcelona nuts, shelled	30 kernels	25	5.7	639	2675	10.9	5.2	1.8	3.4	64.0	–	–	–	0
28 barley, pearl, raw	1 tablespoon	20	10.6	360	1507	7.9	83.6	83.6	0.0	1.7	–	–	–	–
29 basil		5	88.0	40	167	3.1	5.1	0.0	–	0.8	–	–	–	0
30 bass		120	78.6	100	419	19.3	0.0	0.0	0.0	2.5	25.0	37.5	37.5	80
31 beans, aduki, boiled		60	59.4	123	515	9.3	22.5	20.8	0.5	0.2	–	–	–	0

per 100 g	fibre	non-starch polysaccharide	vit A	carotene	vit E	vit B₁	vit B₂	niacin	vit B₆	folate	vit C	sodium	calcium	iron	iodine
	g	g	µg	µg	mg	mg	mg	mg	mg	µg	mg	mg	mg	mg	µg
1 advocaat	0.0	0.0	–	–	–	–	–	1.4	–	–	–	–	–	–	–
2 All-Bran breakfast cereal	30.0	24.5	0	0	2.2	1.00	1.50	19.2	1.80	250	0	1480	69	12.0	–
3 almonds, shelled	12.9	7.4	0	0	24.0	0.21	0.75	6.5	0.15	48	0	14	240	3.0	2
4 anchovies, canned in oil	0.0	0.0	62	0	–	0.00	0.10	8.5	–	18	0	3930	300	4.1	–
5 apple juice, unsweetened	0.0	0.0	0	0	0.0	0.01	0.01	0.1	0.02	4	14	2	7	0.1	0
6 apples, cooking	1.6	1.1	2	12	0.2	0.03	0.01	1.1	0.04	4	10	1	3	0.1	0
7 apples, dessert	1.8	1.6	3	16	0.5	0.03	0.02	0.2	0.05	1	5	3	4	0.1	0
8 apricots	1.7	1.6	63	375	–	0.04	0.05	0.6	0.07	5	5	2	14	0.5	–
9 apricots, canned in juice	1.2	0.9	35	210	–	0.20	0.01	0.4	0.06	2	14	5	21	0.4	7
10 apricots, canned in syrup	1.2	0.9	26	155	–	0.01	0.01	0.4	0.06	2	5	10	19	0.2	7
11 apricots, dried	21.6	7.7	108	645	–	0.00	0.20	3.6	0.17	14	0	56	92	4.1	–
12 artichoke, globe	–	–	7	39	0.1	0.00	0.01	0.6	0.01	21	0	6	19	0.2	–
13 artichoke, Jerusalem	–	3.5	3	20	0.2	0.10	0.00	1.3	–	–	2	3	30	0.4	–
14 asparagus	1.4	1.4	88	530	1.2	0.12	0.06	1.4	0.07	155	10	60	25	0.6	0
15 aubergine	2.3	2.0	12	70	0.0	0.02	0.01	0.3	0.08	18	4	2	10	0.3	1
16 avocado	–	2.4	2	11	2.3	0.07	0.13	1.0	0.26	8	4	4	8	0.3	1
17 babaco	–	–	29	175	–	0.03	0.04	0.7	–	–	26	2	11	0.4	–
18 bacon collar joint, boiled	0.0	0.0	0	0	0.1	0.37	0.30	8.5	0.33	1	0	1350	15	1.9	12
19 bacon rasher, back grilled	0.0	0.0	0	0	0.1	0.43	0.17	9.2	0.27	1	0	2020	12	1.5	11
20 bacon rasher, middle, grilled	0.0	0.0	0	0	0.1	0.41	0.16	9.0	0.26	1	0	2000	12	1.5	10
21 bacon rasher, streaky, grilled	0.0	0.0	0	0	0.1	0.40	0.16	8.8	0.25	1	0	1990	12	1.5	9
22 bacon, gammon joint, boiled	0.0	0.0	0	0	0.1	0.55	0.19	9.7	0.33	1	0	1110	10	1.5	6
23 bacon, gammon steak, grilled	0.0	0.0	0	0	0.0	1.00	0.27	13.0	0.37	2	0	2210	10	1.5	6
24 banana	2.0	0.7	2	14	0.2	0.03	0.04	0.6	0.19	9	7	1	4	0.2	5
25 banana, green (matoki)	2.0	1.5	9	51	–	0.05	0.08	0.6	0.27	44	8	130	3	0.3	–
26 barbecue sauce	–	–	87	520	–	0.03	0.02	1.2	–	–	7	810	19	0.9	–
27 Barcelona nuts, shelled	9.3	–	0	0	–	0.11	–	–	–	–	0	3	170	3.0	–
28 barley, pearl, raw	5.9	–	0	0	0.4	0.12	0.05	4.8	0.22	20	0	3	20	3.0	–
29 basil	–	–	658	3950	–	0.08	0.31	1.1	–	–	26	9	250	5.5	–
30 bass	0.0	0.0	0	0	–	–	–	–	–	–	0	69	130	2.2	–
31 beans, aduki, boiled	–	5.5	1	6	–	0.14	0.08	2.4	–	–	0	2	39	1.9	–

per 100 g		average serving g	water g	energy kcal	energy kJ	protein g	carbohydrates g	starch g	sugars g	fat g	saturated %	mono-unsaturated %	poly-unsaturated %	cholesterol mg
32 beans, baked, canned	small tin	150	71.5	84	352	5.2	15.3	9.4	5.9	0.6	20.0	20.0	60.0	0
33 beans, baked, canned, low sugar,salt	small tin	150	73.6	73	306	5.4	12.5	9.7	2.8	0.6	20.0	20.0	60.0	0
34 beans, black gram, boiled		120	71.3	89	373	7.8	13.6	13.0	0.3	0.4	25.0	25.0	50.0	0
35 beans, blackeye, boiled		60	66.2	116	486	8.8	19.9	18.0	1.1	0.7	33.3	16.7	50.0	0
36 beans, broad beans		120	73.8	81	339	7.9	11.7	10.0	1.3	0.6	20.0	20.0	60.0	0
37 beans, butter beans, canned		60	74.0	77	322	5.9	13.0	10.9	1.1	0.5	–	–	–	0
38 beans, French		90	90.7	24	100	1.9	3.2	0.9	2.3	0.5	–	–	–	0
39 beans, haricot, boiled		60	69.6	95	398	6.6	17.2	15.8	0.8	0.5	–	–	–	0
40 beans, mung, boiled (dahl)		60	69.3	91	381	7.6	15.3	14.1	0.5	0.4	–	–	–	0
41 beans, pinto beans, boiled		60	62.5	137	573	8.9	23.9	–	–	0.7	16.7	8.3	75.0	0
42 beans, red kidney, boiled		60	66.0	103	431	8.4	17.4	14.5	1.0	0.5	–	–	–	0
43 beans, runner		90	92.8	18	75	1.2	2.3	0.3	2.0	0.5	–	–	–	0
44 beans, soya, boiled		60	64.3	141	590	14.0	5.1	1.9	2.1	7.3	15.5	24.1	60.3	0
45 beansprouts		20	90.4	31	130	2.9	4.0	1.8	2.2	0.5	–	–	–	0
46 beansprouts, alfalfa		20	93.4	24	100	4.0	0.4	0.0	0.3	0.7	–	–	–	0
47 beef, brisket, boiled		100	48.4	326	1365	27.6	0.0	0.0	0.0	23.9	43.6	54.1	2.3	91
48 beef, canned stewed steak		100	70.0	176	737	14.8	1.0	1.0	0.0	12.5	50.0	46.6	3.4	57
49 beef, forerib, roast		100	59.1	225	942	27.9	0.0	0.0	0.0	12.6	45.2	50.4	4.3	82
50 beef, rump steak, grilled		100	63.8	168	703	28.6	0.0	0.0	0.0	6.0	45.5	50.9	3.6	82
51 beef, salt silverside		100	59.7	173	724	32.3	0.0	0.0	0.0	4.9	44.4	51.1	4.4	82
52 beef, salted ox tongue	2 slices	50	48.6	293	1226	19.5	0.0	0.0	0.0	23.9	–	–	–	100
53 beef, sirloin, roast		100	62.0	192	804	27.6	0.0	0.0	0.0	9.1	44.6	50.6	4.8	82
54 beef, stewed mince		100	59.1	229	959	23.1	0.0	0.0	0.0	15.2	44.8	51.0	4.1	83
55 beef, stewing steak		100	57.1	223	933	30.9	0.0	0.0	0.0	11.0	44.8	50.5	4.8	82
56 beef, topside, roast		100	65.1	156	653	29.2	0.0	0.0	0.0	4.4	36.8	57.9	5.3	82
57 beefburger, fried	quarter–pounder	90	53.0	264	1105	20.4	7.0	0.0	0.0	17.3	48.5	47.3	4.2	81
58 beer, bitter	1 pint	570	93.6	32	134	0.3	2.3	0.0	2.3	0.0	–	–	–	0
59 beer, lager	1 pint	570	94.4	29	121	0.2	1.5	0.0	1.5	0.0	–	–	–	0
60 beer, stout	1 pint	570	91.3	37	155	0.3	4.2	0.0	4.2	0.0	–	–	–	0
61 beetroot, boiled		35	82.4	46	193	2.3	9.5	0.7	8.8	0.1	–	–	–	0
62 betel (areca nuts)		25	11.5	339	1419	5.2	56.7	–	–	10.2	–	–	–	0
63 bhajia (pakora)		60	56.9	180	753	7.8	20.4	17.9	1.8	8.2	–	–	–	–
64 bhindi (okra, ladies' fingers)		50	87.9	28	117	2.5	2.7	0.5	2.3	0.9	42.9	14.3	42.9	

per 100 g	fibre	non-starch polysaccharide	vit A	carotene	vit E	vit B₁	vit B₂	niacin	vit B₆	folate	vit C	sodium	calcium	iron	iodine
	g	g	µg	µg	mg	mg	mg	mg	mg	µg	mg	mg	mg	mg	µg
32 beans, baked, canned	6.9	3.7	12	74	0.4	0.09	0.06	1.3	0.14	22	0	530	53	1.4	3
33 beans, baked, canned, low sugar, salt	7.1	3.8	13	77	0.4	0.09	0.06	1.4	0.14	23	0	330	45	1.2	3
34 beans, black gram, boiled	5.8	–	2	12	–	0.11	0.09	2.0	–	33	0	13	49	2.0	–
35 beans, blackeye, boiled	–	3.5	2	13	–	0.19	0.05	2.4	0.10	210	0	5	21	1.9	–
36 beans, broad beans	–	6.5	38	225	0.6	0.03	0.06	4.3	0.08	32	8	8	56	1.6	6
37 beans, butter beans, canned	–	4.6	0	0	0.3	0.05	0.03	1.1	0.05	12	0	420	15	1.5	–
38 beans, French	3.0	2.2	55	330	0.2	0.05	0.07	1.4	0.05	80	12	0	36	1.2	–
39 beans, haricot, boiled	6.7	6.1	0	0	0.1	0.10	0.04	1.7	0.12	–	0	15	65	2.5	–
40 beans, mung, boiled (dahl)	4.8	3.0	2	12	–	0.09	0.07	1.7	0.07	35	0	2	24	1.4	–
41 beans, pinto beans, boiled	–		0	0	–	0.23	0.06	1.7	0.15	145	2	1	47	2.3	–
42 beans, red kidney, boiled	9.0	6.7	1	4	0.2	0.17	0.05	1.9	0.12	42	1	2	37	2.5	–
43 beans, runner	3.1	1.9	20	120	0.2	0.05	0.02	0.3	0.04	42	10	1	22	1.0	0
44 beans, soya, boiled	–	6.1	1	6	1.1	0.12	0.09	2.7	0.23	54	0	1	83	3.0	2
45 beansprouts	5.6	1.5	7	40	–	0.11	0.04	1.0	0.10	61	7	5	20	1.7	–
46 beansprouts, alfalfa	–	1.7	16	96	–	0.04	0.06	1.1	0.03	36	2	6	32	1.0	–
47 beef, brisket, boiled	0.0	0.0	0	0	0.4	0.04	0.30	10.2	0.25	13	0	73	12	2.8	6
48 beef, canned stewed steak	0.0	0.0	0	0	0.6	0.00	0.13	5.2	0.07	4	0	380	14	2.1	–
49 beef, forerib, roast	0.0	0.0	0	0	0.3	0.05	0.33	11.5	0.33	17	0	56	13	2.3	6
50 beef, rump steak, grilled	0.0	0.0	0	0	0.3	0.09	0.36	12.5	0.33	17	0	56	7	3.5	6
51 beef, salt silverside	0.0	0.0	0	0	0.3	0.04	0.32	10.8	0.33	17	0	1000	10	3.2	6
52 beef, salted ox tongue	0.0	0.0	0	0	0.4	0.06	0.29	8.3	0.09	5	2	1000	31	3.0	–
53 beef, sirloin, roast	0.0	0.0	0	0	0.3	0.07	0.31	11.9	0.33	17	0	59	10	2.1	6
54 beef, stewed mince	0.0	0.0	0	0	0.3	0.05	0.33	9.3	0.30	16	0	320	18	3.1	6
55 beef, stewing steak	0.0	0.0	0	0	0.3	0.03	0.33	10.2	0.30	16	0	360	15	3.0	6
56 beef, topside, roast	0.0	0.0	0	0	0.3	0.08	0.35	12.7	0.33	17	0	49	6	2.8	6
57 beefburger, fried	0.0	0.0	0	0	0.6	0.02	0.23	8.0	0.20	15	0	880	33	3.1	0
58 beer, bitter	0.0	0.0	0	0	0.0	0.00	0.04	0.6	0.02	9	0	12	11	0.0	8
59 beer, lager	0.0	0.0	0	0	0.0	0.00	0.02	0.5	0.02	4	0	4	4	0.0	–
60 beer, stout	0.0	0.0	0	0	0.0	0.00	0.03	0.4	0.01	4	0	23	8	0.1	–
61 beetroot, boiled	2.3	1.9	5	27	0.0	0.01	0.01	0.4	0.04	110	5	110	29	0.8	–
62 betel (areca nuts)	–	–	0	0		0.19	0.52	1.1	–	–	0	76	400	4.9	–
63 bhajia (pakora)	5.6	4.5	130	–	–	0.15	0.05	1.7	0.16	50	5	360	93	3.4	–
64 bhindi (okra, ladies' fingers)	4.1	3.6	78	465	–	0.13	0.05	1.2	0.19	46	16	5	120	0.6	–

33

per 100 g		average serving	water	energy	energy	protein	carbohydrates	starch	sugars	fat	saturated	mono-unsaturated	poly-unsaturated	cholesterol
		g	g	kcal	kJ	g	g	g	g	g	%	%	%	mg
65 bilberries		110	85.9	30	126	0.6	6.9	0.0	6.9	0.2	–	–	–	0
66 biscuits, chocolate coated	1 biscuit	8	2.2	524	2193	5.7	67.4	24.0	43.4	27.6	64.7	31.0	4.3	22
67 biscuits, cream crackers	1 biscuit	7	4.3	440	1842	9.5	68.3	68.3	0.0	16.3	–	–	–	–
68 biscuits, digestive, chocolate	1 biscuit	18	2.5	493	2064	6.8	66.5	38.0	28.5	24.1	53.3	38.9	7.9	51
69 biscuits, digestive, plain	1 biscuit	13	2.5	471	1972	6.3	68.6	55.0	13.6	20.9	43.2	48.2	8.5	41
70 biscuits, gingernuts	1 biscuit	10	3.4	456	1909	5.6	79.1	43.3	35.8	15.2	50.0	40.3	9.7	–
71 biscuits, oatcakes	1 biscuit	17	5.5	441	1846	10.0	63.0	59.9	3.1	18.3	22.5	47.4	30.1	8
72 biscuits, semisweet	1 biscuit	8	2.5	457	1913	6.7	74.8	52.5	22.3	16.6	51.3	37.8	10.9	31
73 biscuits, shortbread	1 biscuit	13	2.6	469	1963	6.2	62.2	38.1	24.1	23.4	53.2	35.9	10.9	37
74 biscuits, wafer biscuits	1 biscuit	7	2.3	535	2240	4.7	66.0	21.3	44.7	29.9	67.1	29.6	3.2	–
75 biscuits, water biscuits	1 biscuit	8	4.5	440	1842	10.8	75.8	73.5	2.3	12.5	–	–	–	–
76 biscuits, wholemeal crackers	1 biscuit	15	4.4	413	1729	10.1	72.1	70.5	1.6	11.3	–	–	–	–
77 black pudding, fried		85	44.0	305	1277	12.9	15.0	15.0	0.0	21.9	42.1	40.1	17.8	68
78 blackberries		110	85.0	25	105	0.9	5.1	0.0	5.1	0.2	–	–	–	0
79 blackcurrants		110	77.4	28	117	0.9	6.6	0.0	6.6	0.0	–	–	–	0
80 bloater, grilled		120	36.1	163	682	15.3	0.0	0.0	0.0	11.3	29.0	48.0	23.0	43
81 blueberries		110	85.9	30	126	0.6	6.9	0.0	6.9	0.2	–	–	–	0
82 Bombay mix (chevda)		30	3.5	503	2106	18.8	35.1	32.8	2.3	32.9	12.7	51.4	35.9	0
83 Bounty bar	standard bar	57	7.6	473	1980	4.8	58.3	4.6	53.7	26.1	85.5	12.9	1.6	10
84 Bovril		4	38.7	169	707	38.0	2.9	2.9	0.0	0.7	–	–	–	–
85 Bran Buds breakfast cereal		30	3.0	273	1143	13.1	52.0	26.3	25.7	2.9	–	–	–	–
86 Bran Flakes breakfast cereal		20	3.0	319	1335	10.2	69.7	50.7	19.0	1.9	25.0	12.5	62.5	0
87 Brazil nuts, shelled	3 nuts	10	2.8	682	2855	14.1	3.1	0.7	2.4	68.2	25.2	39.6	35.3	0
88 bread, brown	2 slices	70	39.5	218	913	8.5	44.3	41.3	3.0	2.0	30.8	23.1	46.2	0
89 bread, brown crusty roll	1	50	30.5	255	1067	10.3	50.4	48.5	1.9	2.8	31.6	31.6	36.8	0
90 bread, brown soft roll	1	50	31.6	268	1122	10.0	51.8	49.3	2.5	3.8	36.0	32.0	32.0	0
91 bread, brown, toasted	2 slices	60	24.4	272	1139	10.4	56.5	52.1	4.5	2.1	23.1	23.1	53.8	0
92 bread, burger bun	1	85	32.9	264	1105	9.1	48.8	46.6	2.2	5.0	31.4	37.1	31.4	0
93 bread, croissant	1	60	31.1	360	1507	8.3	38.3	37.2	1.0	20.3	33.3	41.5	25.1	75
94 bread, currant	2 slices	70	29.4	289	1210	7.5	50.7	36.3	14.4	7.6	31.4	29.4	39.2	0
95 bread, French loaf (baguette)	6 inch slice	120	29.3	270	1130	9.6	55.4	53.5	1.9	2.7	33.3	27.8	38.9	0
96 bread, granary	2 slices	70	35.4	235	984	9.3	46.3	44.1	2.2	2.7	27.8	33.3	38.9	0
97 bread, Hovis, brown	2 slices	70	40.3	212	887	9.5	41.5	39.7	1.8	2.0	23.1	23.1	53.8	0

per 100 g	fibre	non-starch polysaccharide	vit A	carotene	vit E	vit B₁	vit B₂	niacin	vit B₆	folate	vit C	sodium	calcium	iron	iodine
	g	g	µg	µg	mg	mg	mg	mg	mg	µg	mg	mg	mg	mg	µg
65 bilberries	2.5	1.8	5	30	–	0.03	0.03	0.5	0.05	6	17	3	12	0.5	–
66 biscuits, chocolate coated	2.9	2.1	0	0	1.4	0.03	0.13	1.7	0.04	–	0	160	110	1.7	–
67 biscuits, cream crackers	6.1	2.2	0	0	1.3	0.23	0.05	3.6	0.12	22	0	610	110	1.7	13
68 biscuits, digestive, chocolate	3.1	2.2	0	0	1.1	0.08	0.11	2.7	0.08	–	0	450	84	2.1	–
69 biscuits, digestive, plain	4.6	2.2	0	0	–	0.14	0.11	2.4	0.09	13	0	600	92	3.2	–
70 biscuits, gingernuts	1.8	1.4	0	–	1.5	0.10	0.03	2.0	0.07	4	0	330	130	4.0	–
71 biscuits, oatcakes	3.6	–	0	0	2.1	0.32	0.09	3.0	0.10	26	0	1230	54	4.5	–
72 biscuits, semisweet	2.1	1.7	0	0	1.4	0.13	0.08	2.9	0.06	13	0	410	120	2.1	–
73 biscuits, shortbread	1.5	1.5	0	0	1.3	0.16	0.04	2.2	0.05	13	0	360	87	1.8	–
74 biscuits, wafer biscuits	1.4	–	0	0	1.9	0.09	0.08	1.5	0.03	–	0	70	73	1.6	–
75 biscuits, water biscuits	6.1	3.1	0	0	0.0	0.11	0.03	3.1	0.06	–	0	470	120	1.6	–
76 biscuits, wholemeal crackers	4.8	4.4	0	0	1.5	0.26	0.06	4.7	0.18	26	0	700	110	2.5	–
77 black pudding, fried	0.5	0.0	41	0	0.2	0.09	0.07	3.8	0.04	5	0	1210	35	20.0	–
78 blackberries	6.6	3.1	13	80	2.4	0.02	0.05	0.6	0.05	34	15	2	41	0.7	–
79 blackcurrants	7.8	3.6	17	100	1.0	0.03	0.06	0.4	0.08	–	200	3	60	1.3	–
80 bloater, grilled	0.0	0.0	24	0	0.7	0.00	0.18	5.5	0.23	6	0	450	56	1.1	–
81 blueberries	2.5	1.8	5	30	–	0.03	0.03	0.5	0.05	6	17	3	12	0.5	–
82 Bombay mix (chevda)	–	6.2	0	0	4.7	0.38	0.10	7.8	0.54	–	0	770	58	3.8	–
83 Bounty bar	–	–	7	40	–	0.04	0.10	1.1	0.03	–	0	180	110	1.3	–
84 Bovril	0.0	0.0	0	0	–	9.10	7.40	85.0	0.53	1040	0	4800	40	14.0	–
85 Bran Buds breakfast cereal	28.2	20.0	0	0	–	1.00	1.50	18.8	1.80	250	0	510	56	12.0	–
86 Bran Flakes breakfast cereal	17.3	11.3	0	0	–	1.00	1.50	18.4	1.80	250	35	910	50	40.0	–
87 Brazil nuts, shelled	8.1	4.3	0	0	7.2	0.67	0.03	3.3	0.31	21	0	3	170	2.5	20
88 bread, brown	5.9	3.5	0	0	0.0	0.27	0.09	4.2	0.13	40	0	540	100	2.2	–
89 bread, brown crusty roll	7.1	3.5	0	0	0.0	0.43	0.07	5.6	0.09	54	0	570	100	3.2	–
90 bread, brown soft roll	6.4	3.5	0	0	0.0	0.41	0.08	5.4	0.09	29	0	560	110	3.4	–
91 bread, brown, toasted	7.1	4.5	0	0	0.0	0.26	0.12	5.2	0.14	44	0	690	140	2.7	–
92 bread, burger bun	4.0	1.5	0	0	0.0	0.23	0.10	3.4	0.06	48	0	550	130	2.3	19
93 bread, croissant	2.5	1.6	21	0	0.0	0.18	0.16	3.8	0.11	73	0	390	80	2.0	–
94 bread, currant	3.8	–	0	0	0.0	0.19	0.09	3.0	0.09	19	0	290	86	1.6	29
95 bread, French loaf (baguette)	5.1	1.5	0	0	0.0	0.19	0.07	3.3	0.08	24	0	570	130	2.1	6
96 bread, granary	6.5	4.3	0	0	–	0.30	0.11	4.9	0.17	90	0	580	77	2.7	–
97 bread, Hovis, brown	5.1	3.3	0	0	–	0.80	0.09	6.1	0.11	39	0	600	120	3.7	22

per 100 g	average serving	water	energy	energy	protein	carbohydrates	starch	sugars	fat	saturated	mono-unsaturated	poly-unsaturated	cholesterol
	g	g	kcal	kJ	g	g	g	g	g	%	%	%	mg
98 bread, Hovis, brown, toasted	2 slices	60	23.5	271	1134	12.1	53.2	50.9	2.3	2.6	23.1	23.1	53.8	0
99 bread, malt	2 slices	70	25.8	268	1122	8.3	56.8	30.7	26.1	2.4	18.8	18.8	62.5	1
100 bread, naan	1	160	28.8	336	1406	8.9	50.1	44.6	5.5	12.5	–	–	–	6
101 bread, pitta	large	95	32.7	265	1109	9.2	57.9	55.5	2.4	1.2	25.0	12.5	62.5	0
102 bread, rye	2 slices	50	37.4	219	917	8.3	45.8	44.0	1.8	1.7	25.0	25.0	50.0	0
103 bread, Scottish batch	1 thick slice	50	36.5	238	996	8.7	51.1	48.5	2.6	1.3	–	–	–	–
104 bread, soda bread	1 farl	130	36.0	258	1080	7.7	54.6	51.7	2.9	2.5	–	–	–	–
105 bread, Vienna		50	32.6	263	1101	9.3	52.2	50.5	1.7	3.3	–	–	–	–
106 bread, Vitbe	2 slices	70	37.5	229	959	9.7	43.4	40.4	3.0	3.1	28.6	28.6	42.9	0
107 bread, West Indian		75	33.2	284	1189	8.3	58.8	51.8	7.0	3.4	–	–	–	–
108 bread, white	1 thick slice	50	37.3	235	984	8.4	49.3	46.7	2.6	1.9	30.8	30.8	38.5	0
109 bread, white crusty roll	1	50	26.4	280	1172	10.9	57.6	55.4	2.2	2.3	33.3	26.7	40.0	0
110 bread, white sliced	2 slices	70	40.4	217	908	7.6	46.8	43.8	3.0	1.3	33.3	22.2	44.4	0
111 bread, white soft roll	1	45	32.7	268	1122	9.2	51.6	49.4	2.2	4.2	37.0	37.0	25.9	0
112 bread, white, added fibre	2 slices	70	40.0	230	963	7.6	49.6	46.3	3.3	1.5	30.8	46.2	23.1	0
113 bread, white, toasted	1 thick slice	60	27.3	265	1109	9.3	57.1	53.4	3.7	1.6	30.8	30.8	38.5	0
114 bread, wholemeal	2 slices	70	38.3	215	900	9.2	41.6	39.8	1.8	2.5	29.4	29.4	41.2	0
115 bread, wholemeal roll	1	48	31.2	241	1009	9.0	48.3	46.8	1.5	2.9	33.3	38.1	28.6	0
116 bread, wholemeal, toasted	2 slices	60	27.8	252	1055	10.8	48.7	46.6	2.1	2.9	28.6	28.6	42.9	0
117 breadfruit		200	64.7	119	498	1.6	29.0	27.5	1.5	0.4	–	–	–	0
118 bream		120	77.7	96	402	17.5	0.0	0.0	0.0	2.9	–	–	–	38
119 broccoli		85	91.1	24	100	3.1	1.1	0.0	0.9	0.8	28.6	14.3	57.1	0
120 brown sauce	1 portion pack	20	64.0	99	414	1.1	25.2	2.1	23.1	0.0	–	–	–	0
121 Brussels sprouts		90	86.9	35	147	2.9	3.5	0.3	3.0	1.3	27.3	9.1	63.6	0
122 bullock's heart (custard apple)	100	75.8	70	293	1.5	16.1	1.2	14.9	0.4	–	–	–	0	
123 bun, Chelsea	1	80	20.1	366	1532	7.8	56.1	34.7	21.4	13.8	31.8	40.2	28.0	55
124 bun, currant	1	60	27.7	296	1239	7.6	52.7	37.6	15.1	7.5	–	–	–	17
125 bun, hot cross	1	50	25.2	310	1298	7.4	58.5	35.1	23.4	6.8	35.0	38.3	26.7	31
126 Burger King Broiler		170	–	226	944	14.3	18.5	–	–	10.7	20.3	53.8	25.9	32
127 Burger King Broiler sauce		14	–	643	2691	0.0	0.0	–	0.0	71.4	12.5	25.0	62.5	50
128 Burger King bacon double cheeseburger de luxe		195	–	304	1271	16.9	14.4	–	–	20.0	44.4	38.9	16.7	57
129 Burger King barbecue bacon double cheese		175	–	308	1289	18.4	17.8	–	–	17.8	48.3	44.8	6.9	60

per 100 g	fibre	non-starch polysaccharide	vit A	carotene	vit E	vit B₁	vit B₂	niacin	vit B₆	folate	vit C	sodium	calcium	iron	iodine
	g	g	µg	µg	mg	mg	mg	mg	mg	µg	mg	mg	mg	mg	µg
98 bread, Hovis, brown, toasted	6.5	4.2	0	0	–	0.87	0.12	8.0	0.14	50	0	770	150	4.7	28
99 bread, malt	6.5	–	0	0	–	0.45	0.13	4.5	0.11	30	0	280	110	2.8	27
100 bread, naan	2.2	1.9	96	60	1.4	0.19	0.10	3.0	0.13	14	0	380	160	1.3	19
101 bread, pitta	3.9	2.2	0	0	–	0.24	0.05	3.3	–	21	0	520	91	1.7	–
102 bread, rye	5.8	4.4	0	0	1.2	0.29	0.05	4.0	0.09	24	0	580	80	2.5	–
103 bread, Scottish batch	3.9	1.5	0	0	0.0	0.18	0.03	3.0	0.05	21	0	710	130	1.8	6
104 bread, soda bread	2.4	2.1	22	–	0.2	0.17	0.08	2.7	0.09	9	0	420	140	1.4	16
105 bread, Vienna	4.1	1.5	0	0	0.0	0.27	0.08	3.5	0.08	21	0	540	110	2.4	6
106 bread, Vitbe	5.8	3.3	0	0	–	0.23	0.10	3.7	0.18	53	0	550	150	2.1	22
107 bread, West Indian	4.8	1.9	0	0	0.0	0.16	0.03	2.9	0.07	25	0	450	150	2.6	6
108 bread, white	3.8	1.5	0	0	0.0	0.21	0.06	3.4	0.07	29	0	520	110	1.6	6
109 bread, white crusty roll	4.3	1.5	0	0	0.0	0.26	0.05	4.3	0.04	32	0	640	140	2.1	19
110 bread, white sliced	3.7	1.5	0	0	0.0	0.20	0.05	3.1	0.07	17	0	530	100	1.4	6
111 bread, white soft roll	3.9	1.5	0	0	0.0	0.28	0.04	3.8	0.04	24	0	560	120	2.2	19
112 bread, white, added fibre	–	3.1	0	0	0.0	0.20	0.05	3.1	0.07	17	0	450	150	2.3	6
113 bread, white, toasted	4.5	1.8	0	0	0.0	0.21	0.06	4.7	0.09	21	0	650	120	1.7	7
114 bread, wholemeal	7.4	5.8	0	0	0.2	0.34	0.09	5.9	0.12	39	0	550	54	2.7	0
115 bread, wholemeal roll	8.8	5.9	0	0	0.2	0.30	0.09	5.9	0.10	62	0	460	55	3.5	0
116 bread, wholemeal, toasted	8.7	5.9	0	0	0.2	0.34	0.10	6.9	0.14	46	0	640	63	3.2	0
117 breadfruit	–	–	5	30	–	0.08	0.05	0.7	–	–	20	1	18	0.9	–
118 bream	0.0	0.0	0	0	–	0.08	0.10	8.7	0.46	–	0	110	40	0.5	–
119 broccoli	–	2.3	79	475	1.1	0.05	0.05	1.3	0.11	64	44	13	40	1.0	2
120 brown sauce	–	0.7	7	40	–	0.13	0.09	0.3	0.10	8	0	980	43	3.1	–
121 Brussels sprouts	2.6	3.1	53	320	0.9	0.07	0.09	0.5	0.19	110	60	2	20	0.5	1
122 bullock's heart (custard apple)	–	–	5	29	–	0.09	0.08	0.6	0.22·	–	21	5	24	0.6	–
123 bun, Chelsea	2.2	1.7	17	1	1.5	0.16	0.13	3.0	0.11	32	0	330	110	1.5	–
124 bun, currant	1.8	–	0	–	–	0.37	0.16	3.1	0.11	40	0	230	110	1.9	–
125 bun, hot cross	2.2	1.7	72	43	0.7	0.15	0.11	2.8	0.10	28	0	120	110	1.6	–
126 Burger King Broiler	1.1	0.0	71	271	1.8	0.16	0.16	3.1	0.14	22	4	455	44	1.9	–
127 Burger King Broiler sauce	0.0	0.0	0	–	–	–	–	–	–	–	–	679	–	–	–
128 Burger King bacon double cheeseburger de luxe	0.5	0.0	65	169	0.9	0.15	0.20	4.2	0.19	16	4	412	80	2.0	–
129 Burger King barbecue bacon double cheese	0.5	0.0	35	42	0.4	0.17	0.23	4.7	0.20	16	3	457	91	2.3	–

per 100 g		average serving	water	energy	energy	protein	carbohydrates	starch	sugars	fat	saturated	mono-unsaturated	poly-unsaturated	cholesterol
		g	g	kcal	kJ	g	g	g	g	g	%	%	%	mg
130 Burger King Chicken Tenders		90	–	44	183	3.0	2.6	–	–	2.4	27.3	45.4	27.3	9
131 Burger King double cheeseburger		170	–	281	1175	17.4	16.9	–	–	15.7	50.0	42.3	7.7	58
132 Burger King egg and cheese croissant		125	–	291	1216	10.1	19.1	–	–	19.4	61.3	32.8	6.0	170
133 Burger King egg, cheese and ham croissant		150	–	313	1308	12.4	15.9	–	–	22.1	56.0	36.5	7.5	140
134 Burger King Fish Tenders		100	–	270	1129	12.1	18.2	–	–	16.2	21.4	50.0	28.6	28
135 Burger King mushroom Swiss double cheese		175	–	269	1125	17.6	15.3	–	–	15.3	48.0	44.0	8.0	54
136 Burger King Ranch dip sauce		28	–	611	2556	0.0	7.1	–	–	64.3	17.6	23.5	58.8	0
137 Burger King sweet and sour sauce		28	–	161	673	0.0	39.3	–	–	0.0	–	–	–	0
138 Burger King tartar dip sauce		28	–	621	2601	0.0	10.7	–	–	64.3	16.7	22.2	61.1	57
139 Burger King Tater Tenders		70	–	300	1256	2.8	35.2	–	–	16.9	25.0	50.0	25.0	4
140 Burger King Whopper hamburger		260	–	241	1010	10.0	19.2	–	4.6	13.8	50.7	42.4	6.8	40
141 butter		15	15.6	737	3085	0.5	0.0	0.0	0.0	81.7	70.7	25.9	3.4	230
142 butter, unsalted		15	15.7	751	3144	0.5	0.0	0.0	0.0	82.7	70.7	25.9	3.4	233
143 cabbage, Chinese leaves		40	95.4	12	50	1.0	1.4	0.0	1.4	0.2	–	–	–	0
144 cabbage, green		95	90.1	26	109	1.7	4.1	0.1	4.0	0.4	–	–	–	0
145 cabbage, red		95	90.7	21	88	1.1	3.7	0.1	3.3	0.3	–	–	–	0
146 cabbage, white		95	90.7	27	113	1.4	5.0	0.1	4.9	0.2	–	–	–	0
147 cake, gateau	1 slice	85	35.1	337	1411	5.7	43.4	11.0	32.3	16.8	60.9	34.0	5.1	148
148 cake, Madeira	1 slice	40	20.2	393	1645	5.4	58.4	21.9	36.5	16.9	55.0	35.6	9.4	–
149 cake, plain fruit	1 slice	90	19.5	354	1482	5.1	75.9	14.8	43.1	12.9	47.9	43.0	9.1	–
150 cake, rich fruit	1 slice	70	17.6	341	1427	3.8	59.6	11.2	48.4	11.0	32.4	41.9	25.7	63
151 cake, sponge	1 slice	60	15.2	459	1921	6.4	52.4	22.0	30.4	26.3	32.0	42.0	26.0	152
152 cake, sponge, fatless	1 slice	70	31.5	294	1231	10.1	53.0	22.1	30.9	6.1	34.0	50.0	16.0	223
153 Cape gooseberry (physalis, Chinese lantern)	5	10	82.9	53	222	1.8	11.1	0.0	11.1	0.2	–	–	–	0
154 carambola (starfruit, star apple)	3 slices	15	91.4	32	134	0.5	7.3	0.2	7.1	0.3	–	–	–	0
155 carp		100	77.3	112	469	17.5	0.0	0.0	0.0	4.7	27.3	48.5	24.2	67
156 carrots		60	90.5	24	100	0.6	4.9	0.2	4.6	0.4	33.3	0.0	66.7	0
157 cashew nuts, unsalted		25	4.4	573	2399	17.7	18.1	13.5	4.6	48.2	20.6	60.3	19.1	0
158 cassava meal (gari)		–	10.4	358	1499	1.3	92.9	91.9	1.0	0.5	–	–	–	0

per 100 g	fibre	non-starch polysaccharide	vit A	carotene	vit E	vit B₁	vit B₂	niacin	vit B₆	folate	vit C	sodium	calcium	iron	iodine
	g	g	µg	µg	mg	mg	mg	mg	mg	µg	mg	mg	mg	mg	µg
130 Burger King Chicken Tenders	0.3	0.0	0	–	0.4	0.15	0.13	6.9	0.35	10	0	100	10	1.1	–
131 Burger King double cheeseburger	0.8	0.0	108	299	1.2	0.13	0.18	2.9	0.14	18	3	495	110	1.7	–
132 Burger King egg and cheese croissant	1.6	0.0	276	238	0.7	0.15	0.30	1.2	0.08	28	0	434	192	1.7	–
133 Burger King egg, cheese and ham croissant	–	0.0	89	–	–	0.34	0.20	2.1	0.15	24	8	711	95	1.4	–
134 Burger King Fish Tenders	1.1	0.0	20	0	1.6	0.23	0.17	2.3	0.06	23	0	879	61	1.7	–
135 Burger King mushroom Swiss double cheese	–	0.0	–	–	–	–	–	–	–	–	–	424	–	2.4	–
136 Burger King Ranch dip sauce	–	0.0	–	–	–	–	–	–	–	–	–	743	–	–	–
137 Burger King sweet and sour sauce	0.1	0.0	0	–	–	0.00	0.01	0.2	0.01	1	0	186	4	0.4	–
138 Burger King tartar dip sauce	0.2	0.0	118	164	16.7	0.01	0.02	0.0	0.27	8	1	1079	25	0.9	–
139 Burger King Tater Tenders	–	0.0	–	–	–	–	–	–	–	–	–	448	–	–	–
140 Burger King Whopper hamburger	1.0	0.0	120	276	1.8	0.01	0.01	2.0	0.12	12	5	379	40	2.3	–
141 butter	0.0	0.0	887	430	2.0	0.00	0.02	0.1	0.00	0	0	750	15	0.2	38
142 butter, unsalted	0.0	0.0	887	430	2.0	0.00	0.02	0.1	0.00	0	0	11	15	0.2	38
143 cabbage, Chinese leaves	–	1.2	12	70	–	0.09	0.00	0.4	0.11	77	21	7	54	0.6	–
144 cabbage, green	2.9	2.4	64	385	0.2	0.15	0.02	0.8	0.17	75	49	5	52	0.7	2
145 cabbage, red	3.1	2.5	3	15	0.2	0.02	0.01	0.6	0.09	39	55	8	60	0.4	2
146 cabbage, white	2.4	2.1	7	40	0.2	0.12	0.01	0.5	0.18	34	35	7	49	0.5	2
147 cake, gateau	0.5	0.4	265	88	0.8	0.07	0.18	1.8	0.05	11	0	56	60	0.9	17
148 cake, Madeira	1.3	0.9	–	–	–	0.06	0.11	1.6	–	–	0	380	42	1.1	–
149 cake, plain fruit	2.5	–	–	–	–	0.08	0.07	1.6	0.11	8	0	250	60	1.7	–
150 cake, rich fruit	3.2	1.7	125	91	1.3	0.08	0.07	1.4	0.11	8	0	200	82	1.9	–
151 cake, sponge	1.0	0.9	311	215	2.8	0.09	0.12	2.1	0.06	10	0	350	66	1.2	25
152 cake, sponge, fatless	1.0	0.9	110	–	1.0	0.11	0.24	3.2	0.08	18	0	82	75	1.7	34
153 Cape gooseberry (physalis, Chinese lantern)	–	–	238	1430	–	0.05	0.02	0.6	–	–	49	1	10	2.0	–
154 carambola (starfruit, star apple)	1.7	1.3	6	37	–	0.03	0.03	0.4	–	–	31	2	5	0.6	–
155 carp	0.0	0.0	–	0	0.6	0.09	0.07	5.8	0.17	–	0	43	47	0.9	–
156 carrots	2.8	2.5	1260	7560	0.6	0.09	0.00	0.1	0.10	16	2	50	24	0.4	2
157 cashew nuts, unsalted	–	3.2	1	6	0.9	0.69	0.14	5.7	0.49	67	0	15	32	6.2	11
158 cassava meal (gari)	2.9	–	0	0	0.1	0.03	1.00	0.3	0.00	–	7	–	37	3.1	–

per 100 g		average serving	water	energy	energy	protein	carbohydrates	starch	sugars	fat	saturated	mono-unsaturated	poly-unsaturated	cholesterol
		g	g	kcal	kJ	g	g	g	g	g	%	%	%	mg
159 cassava, baked		100	61.3	155	649	0.7	40.1	38.5	1.6	0.2	–	–	–	0
160 cauliflower		90	90.6	28	117	2.9	2.1	0.2	1.8	0.9	25.0	12.5	62.5	0
161 cauliflower cheese		200	78.6	105	440	5.9	5.1	2.1	3.0	6.9	52.3	32.3	15.4	16
162 celeriac		50	88.8	18	75	1.2	2.3	0.5	1.8	0.4	–	–	–	0
163 celery	1 stick	30	95.1	7	29	0.5	0.9	0.0	0.9	0.2	–	–	–	0
164 chapatis made with fat	1	60	28.5	328	1373	8.1	48.3	46.5	1.8	12.8	–	–	–	–
165 chapatis made without fat	1	55	45.8	202	846	7.3	43.7	42.1	1.6	1.0	16.7	16.7	66.7	0
166 chard, Swiss		90	92.7	20	84	1.9	3.2	2.8	0.4	0.1	–	–	–	0
167 chayote (cho cho, christophene)	100	95.0	14	59	0.5	2.9	0.4	2.5	0.1	–	–	–	0	
168 cheese spread	portion	17	53.3	276	1155	13.5	4.4	0.0	4.4	22.8	66.2	30.6	3.2	65
169 cheese, brie		40	48.6	319	1335	19.3	0.0	0.0	0.0	26.9	66.1	30.7	3.1	100
170 cheese, camembert		40	50.7	297	1243	20.9	0.0	0.0	0.0	23.7	66.1	30.8	3.1	75
171 cheese, cheddar		40	36.0	412	1725	25.5	0.1	0.0	0.1	34.4	66.8	28.9	4.3	100
172 cheese, cheddar, reduced fat		40	47.1	261	1093	31.5	0.0	0.0	0.0	15.0	66.2	31.0	2.8	43
173 cheese, Cheshire		40	40.6	379	1586	24.0	0.1	0.0	0.1	31.4	66.2	30.7	3.0	90
174 cheese, Cheshire, reduced fat		40	46.9	269	1126	32.7	0.0	0.0	0.0	15.3	66.2	31.0	2.8	44
175 cheese, cottage	small pot	112	79.1	98	410	13.8	2.1	0.0	2.1	3.9	66.7	30.6	2.8	13
176 cheese, cottage, reduced fat	small pot	112	80.2	78	327	13.3	3.3	0.0	3.3	1.4	69.2	30.8	0.0	5
177 cheese, cream		30	45.5	439	1838	3.1	0.0	0.0	0.0	47.4	66.3	30.6	3.1	95
178 cheese, Danish blue		30	45.3	347	1453	20.1	0.0	0.0	0.0	29.6	66.1	30.7	3.2	75
179 cheese, Derby		40	38.0	402	1683	24.2	0.1	0.0	0.1	33.9	66.3	30.6	3.1	100
180 cheese, double Gloucester		40	37.3	405	1695	24.6	0.1	0.0	0.1	34.0	66.1	30.7	3.1	100
181 cheese, Edam		40	43.8	333	1394	26.0	0.0	0.0	0.0	25.4	66.3	30.8	2.9	80
182 cheese, Emmental		40	35.7	382	1599	28.7	0.0	0.0	0.0	29.7	66.2	30.6	3.2	90
183 cheese, Feta		30	56.5	250	1047	15.6	1.5	0.0	1.5	20.2	74.5	22.3	3.3	70
184 cheese, goat		40	65.0	198	829	13.1	1.0	0.0	1.0	15.8	71.7	24.8	3.4	–
185 cheese, Gouda		40	40.1	375	1570	24.0	0.0	0.0	0.0	31.0	66.2	30.7	3.1	100
186 cheese, Gruyere		40	35.0	409	1712	27.2	0.0	0.0	0.0	33.3	66.0	30.8	3.2	100
187 cheese, Lancashire		40	41.7	373	1561	23.3	0.1	0.0	0.1	31.0	66.2	30.7	3.1	90
188 cheese, Leicester		40	37.5	401	1679	24.3	0.1	0.0	0.1	33.7	66.1	30.7	3.1	100
189 cheese, Parmesan		20	18.4	452	1892	39.4	0.0	0.0	0.0	32.7	66.3	30.7	2.9	100
190 cheese, processed		20	45.7	330	1381	20.8	0.9	0.0	0.9	27.0	65.1	30.2	4.7	85
191 cheese, quark		55	80.4	74	310	14.6	4.0	0.0	4.0	0.0	–	–	–	1

per 100 g	fibre	non-starch polysaccharide	vit A	carotene	vit E	vit B₁	vit B₂	niacin	vit B₆	folate	vit C	sodium	calcium	iron	iodine
	g	g	µg	µg	mg	mg	mg	mg	mg	µg	mg	mg	mg	mg	µg
159 cassava, baked	1.9	1.7	0	0	–	0.04	0.02	0.4	–	11	17	5	19	0.5	–
160 cauliflower	1.6	1.6	10	60	0.1	0.07	0.04	1.1	0.15	51	27	4	17	0.4	0
161 cauliflower cheese	1.4	1.3	76	79	0.4	0.10	0.10	1.9	0.16	7	7	200	120	0.6	8
162 celeriac	5.1	3.7	4	26	–	0.18	0.02	0.4	0.08	51	14	91	40	0.8	–
163 celery	1.6	1.1	8	50	0.2	0.06	0.01	0.4	0.03	16	8	60	41	0.4	–
164 chapatis made with fat	7.0	–	0	0	–	0.26	0.04	3.4	0.20	15	0	130	66	2.3	–
165 chapatis made without fat	6.4	–	0	0	0.0	0.23	0.04	3.0	0.18	14	0	120	60	2.1	–
166 chard, Swiss	–	–	728	4365	–	0.03	0.09	0.7	–	100	18	180	58	2.3	–
167 chayote (cho cho, christophene)	–	0.9	7	40	–	0.02	0.03	0.5	–	–	11	4	13	0.3	–
168 cheese spread	0.0	0.0	293	105	0.2	0.05	0.36	3.3	0.08	19	0	1060	420	0.2	29
169 cheese, brie	0.0	0.0	320	210	0.8	0.04	0.43	4.9	0.15	58	0	700	540	0.8	–
170 cheese, camembert	0.0	0.0	283	315	0.7	0.05	0.52	5.9	0.22	102	0	650	350	0.2	–
171 cheese, cheddar	0.0	0.0	363	225	0.5	0.03	0.40	6.1	0.10	33	0	670	720	0.3	39
172 cheese, cheddar, reduced fat	0.0	0.0	182	100	0.4	0.03	0.53	7.5	0.13	56	0	670	840	0.2	–
173 cheese, Cheshire	0.0	0.0	387	220	0.7	0.03	0.48	5.8	0.09	40	0	550	560	0.3	46
174 cheese, Cheshire, reduced fat	0.0	0.0	163	80	0.3	0.05	0.56	7.9	0.10	58	0	470	650	0.2	–
175 cheese, cottage	0.0	0.0	46	10	0.1	0.03	0.26	3.3	0.08	27	0	380	73	0.1	–
176 cheese, cottage, reduced fat	0.0	0.0	17	4	0.0	0.03	0.26	3.2	0.08	27	0	380	73	0.1	–
177 cheese, cream	0.0	0.0	422	220	1.0	0.03	0.13	0.8	0.04	11	0	300	98	0.1	–
178 cheese, Danish blue	0.0	0.0	322	250	0.8	0.03	0.41	5.2	0.12	50	0	1260	500	0.2	9
179 cheese, Derby	0.0	0.0	377	220	0.5	0.03	0.41	5.7	0.10	26	0	580	680	0.4	46
180 cheese, double Gloucester	0.0	0.0	378	195	0.6	0.03	0.45	5.9	0.11	30	0	590	660	0.4	46
181 cheese, Edam	0.0	0.0	200	150	0.5	0.03	0.35	6.2	0.09	40	0	1020	770	0.4	–
182 cheese, Emmental	0.0	0.0	343	140	0.4	0.05	0.35	6.9	0.09	20	0	450	970	0.3	–
183 cheese, Feta	0.0	0.0	226	33	0.4	0.04	0.21	3.7	0.07	23	0	1440	360	0.2	–
184 cheese, goat	0.0	0.0	311	3	0.8	0.04	0.63	3.7	0.12	19	0	470	190	0.1	–
185 cheese, Gouda	0.0	0.0	269	145	0.5	0.03	0.30	5.7	0.08	43	0	910	740	0.1	–
186 cheese, Gruyere	0.0	0.0	363	225	0.6	0.03	0.39	6.4	0.11	12	0	670	950	0.3	–
187 cheese, Lancashire	0.0	0.0	361	215	0.7	0.03	0.45	5.6	0.08	44	0	590	560	0.2	46
188 cheese, Leicester	0.0	0.0	364	265	0.4	0.03	0.46	5.8	0.11	24	0	630	660	0.5	46
189 cheese, Parmesan	0.0	0.0	380	210	0.7	0.03	0.44	9.4	0.13	12	0	1090	1200	1.1	–
190 cheese, processed	0.0	0.0	286	95	0.6	0.03	0.28	5.0	0.08	18	0	1320	600	0.5	29
191 cheese, quark	0.0	0.0	2	1	0.0	0.04	0.30	3.6	0.08	45	1	45	120	0.0	4

per 100 g	average serving	water	energy	energy	protein	carbohydrates	starch	sugars	fat	saturated	mono-unsaturated	poly-unsaturated	cholesterol
	g	g	kcal	kJ	g	g	g	g	g	%	%	%	mg
192 cheese, ricotta	110	72.1	144	603	9.4	2.0	0.0	2.0	11.0	68.3	26.7	5.0	50
193 cheese, Roquefort	30	41.3	375	1570	19.7	0.0	0.0	0.0	32.9	68.5	26.5	5.0	90
194 cheese, soft, full fat	40	58.0	313	1310	8.6	0.0	0.0	0.0	31.0	66.2	30.7	3.1	90
195 cheese, soft, medium fat	40	69.5	179	749	9.2	3.1	0.0	3.1	14.5	66.4	30.7	2.9	42
196 cheese, Stilton	30	38.6	411	1720	22.7	0.1	0.0	0.1	35.5	66.3	30.7	3.0	105
197 cheese, Wensleydale	40	41.5	377	1578	23.3	0.1	0.0	0.1	31.5	66.3	30.6	3.0	90
198 cherries	80	68.7	39	163	0.7	9.5	0.0	9.5	0.1	–	–	–	0
199 cherries, glacé	25	23.6	251	1051	0.4	66.4	0.0	66.4	0.0	–	–	–	0
200 chestnuts, weighed with shells 5 nuts	50	42.9	140	586	1.6	30.4	24.6	5.8	2.2	19.0	38.1	42.9	0
201 chevda (Bombay mix)	30	3.5	503	2106	18.8	35.1	32.8	2.3	32.9	12.7	51.4	35.9	0
202 chicken, leg quarter	190	42.4	92	385	15.4	0.0	0.0	0.0	3.4	31.3	50.0	18.8	48
203 chicken, roast, dark meat	100	68.2	155	649	23.1	0.0	0.0	0.0	6.9	32.3	49.2	18.5	97
204 chicken, roast, light meat	100	68.5	142	594	26.5	0.0	0.0	0.0	4.0	31.6	50.0	18.4	56
205 chicken, roast, meat and skin	100	61.9	216	904	22.6	0.0	0.0	0.0	14.0	31.8	49.2	18.9	103
206 chicken, roast, meat only	100	68.4	148	620	24.8	0.0	0.0	0.0	5.4	31.4	49.0	19.6	76
207 chicken, wing quarter	190	34.2	74	310	12.4	0.0	0.0	0.0	2.7	32.0	48.0	20.0	38
208 chickpeas, boiled	90	65.8	121	507	8.4	18.2	16.6	1.0	2.1	12.5	25.0	62.5	0
209 chicory	20	94.3	11	46	0.5	2.8	0.2	0.7	0.6	40.0	0.0	60.0	0
210 Chinese gooseberry (kiwi)	60	72.2	42	176	1.0	9.1	0.3	8.9	0.4	–	–	–	0
211 Chinese lantern (physalis, Cape gooseberry) 5	10	82.9	53	222	1.8	11.1	0.0	11.1	0.2	–	–	–	0
212 Chinese leaves (Chinese cabbage)	40	95.4	12	50	1.0	1.4	0.0	1.4	0.2	–	–	–	0
213 chives	10	91.0	23	96	2.8	1.7	0.0	1.7	0.6	–	–	–	0
214 cho cho (chayote, christophene)	100	95.0	14	59	0.5	2.9	0.4	2.5	0.1	–	–	–	0
215 chocolate, milk small bar	50	2.2	529	2214	8.4	59.4	2.9	56.5	30.3	61.8	33.0	5.2	30
216 chocolate, plain small bar	50	0.6	525	2198	4.7	64.8	5.3	59.5	29.2	61.7	33.9	4.4	9
217 chocolate, white small bar	50	0.6	529	2214	8.0	58.3	0.0	58.3	30.9	62.3	33.9	3.8	–
218 chocolates, filled each	10	5.7	460	1926	4.1	73.3	7.5	65.8	18.8	–	–	–	–
219 Christmas pudding	100	23.6	329	1377	3.0	56.3	10.1	46.2	11.8	56.5	38.0	5.6	36
220 cider, dry 1 pint	570	92.5	36	151	0.0	2.6	0.0	2.6	0.0	–	–	–	0
221 cider, sweet 1 pint	570	91.2	42	176	0.0	4.3	0.0	4.3	0.0	–	–	–	0
222 clementine	80	65.6	28	117	0.7	6.5	0.0	6.5	0.1	–	–	–	0
223 cockles, boiled	25	78.9	48	201	11.3	0.0	0.0	0.0	0.3	–	–	–	53

per 100 g	fibre	non-starch polysaccharide	vit A	carotene	vit E	vit B₁	vit B₂	niacin	vit B₆	folate	vit C	sodium	calcium	iron	iodine
	g	g	µg	µg	mg	mg	mg	mg	mg	µg	mg	mg	mg	mg	µg
192 cheese, ricotta	0.0	0.0	200	92	0.0	0.02	0.19	2.3	0.03	–	0	100	240	0.4	–
193 cheese, Roquefort	0.0	0.0	297	10	0.6	0.04	0.65	5.2	0.09	45	0	1670	530	0.4	–
194 cheese, soft, full fat	0.0	0.0	–	–	–	0.03	0.17	2.1	0.05	13	0	330	110	0.1	–
195 cheese, soft, medium fat	0.0	0.0	224	175	0.8	–	–	–	–	–	0	–	–	–	–
196 cheese, Stilton	0.0	0.0	386	185	0.6	0.03	0.43	5.8	0.16	77	0	930	320	0.3	46
197 cheese, Wensleydale	0.0	0.0	318	260	0.4	0.03	0.46	5.6	0.09	43	0	520	560	0.3	46
198 cherries	1.2	0.7	4	21	0.1	0.02	0.02	0.3	0.04	4	9	1	11	0.2	0
199 cherries, glacé	1.5	0.9	1	7	0.0	0.00	0.00	0.0	0.00	0	0	27	56	0.9	–
200 chestnuts, weighed with shells	5.1	3.4	0	0	1.0	0.12	0.02	0.7	0.28	–	0	9	38	0.7	–
201 chevda (Bombay mix)	–	6.2	0	0	4.7	0.38	0.10	7.8	0.54	–	0	770	58	3.8	–
202 chicken, leg quarter	0.0	0.0	0	0	0.1	0.05	0.12	8.0	0.16	6	0	50	6	0.5	5
203 chicken, roast, dark meat	0.0	0.0	0	0	0.2	0.09	0.24	10.4	0.16	13	0	91	9	1.0	5
204 chicken, roast, light meat	0.0	0.0	0	0	0.1	0.08	0.14	15.3	0.35	7	0	71	9	0.5	5
205 chicken, roast, meat and skin	0.0	0.0	0	0	–	–	–	–	–	–	0	72	9	0.8	5
206 chicken, roast, meat only	0.0	0.0	0	0	0.1	0.08	0.19	12.8	0.26	10	0	81	9	0.8	5
207 chicken, wing quarter	0.0	0.0	0	0	0.1	0.04	0.10	6.4	0.13	5	0	41	5	0.4	5
208 chickpeas, boiled	5.1	4.3	4	23	1.1	0.10	0.07	1.8	0.14	54	0	5	46	2.1	–
209 chicory	–	0.9	20	120	–	0.14	0.00	0.3	0.01	14	5	1	21	0.4	–
210 Chinese gooseberry (kiwi)	–	1.6	5	32	–	0.01	0.03	0.6	0.13	–	51	3	21	0.3	–
211 Chinese lantern (physalis, Cape gooseberry)	–	–	238	1430	–	0.05	0.02	0.6	–	–	49	1	10	2.0	–
212 Chinese leaves (Chinese cabbage)	–	1.2	12	70	–	0.09	0.00	0.4	0.11	77	21	7	54	0.6	–
213 chives	–	1.9	383	2300	1.6	0.10	0.18	1.4	0.20	–	45	5	85	1.6	–
214 cho cho (chayote, christophene)	–	0.9	7	40	–	0.02	0.03	0.5	–	–	11	4	13	0.3	–
215 chocolate, milk	0.0	0.0	7	40	0.7	0.10	0.23	1.6	0.07	10	0	120	220	1.6	–
216 chocolate, plain	–	–	7	40	0.9	0.07	0.08	1.2	0.07	10	0	11	38	2.4	–
217 chocolate, white	0.0	0.0	13	75	1.1	0.08	0.49	2.8	0.07	10	0	110	270	0.2	–
218 chocolates, filled	–	–	7	40	–	0.08	0.35	1.0	0.05	10	0	60	92	1.8	120
219 Christmas pudding	3.4	1.7	25	9	0.6	0.08	0.08	1.7	0.08	8	0	170	35	1.2	–
220 cider, dry	0.0	0.0	0	0	0.0	0.00	0.00	0.0	0.01	–	0	7	8	0.5	–
221 cider, sweet	0.0	0.0	0	0	0.0	0.00	0.00	0.0	0.01	–	0	7	8	0.5	–
222 clementine	1.3	0.9	10	57	–	0.07	0.03	0.3	0.05	25	41	3	23	0.1	–
223 cockles, boiled	0.0	0.0	–	11	–	–	–	–	–	–	0	3520	130	26.0	160

per 100 g		average serving	water	energy	energy	protein	carbohydrates	starch	sugars	fat	saturated	mono-unsaturated	poly-unsaturated	cholesterol
		g	g	kcal	kJ	g	g	g	g	g	%	%	%	mg
224 Coco Pops		20	3.0	386	1616	5.3	93.9	55.7	38.2	1.4	44.4	22.2	33.3	0
225 cocoa powder	1 tsp	6	3.4	312	1306	18.5	11.5	11.5	0.0	21.7	62.1	35.0	2.9	0
226 coconut		50	45.0	351	1469	3.2	3.7	0.0	3.7	36.0	91.7	5.9	2.4	0
227 coconut, desiccated		–	2.3	604	2528	5.6	6.4	0.0	6.4	62.0	91.7	5.9	2.4	0
228 cod		120	80.8	80	335	18.3	0.0	0.0	0.0	0.7	20.0	20.0	60.0	46
229 cod roe, battered, fried		160	64.4	189	791	12.4	8.9	8.9	0.0	11.8	–	–	–	330
230 cod, battered, fried		180	60.9	199	833	19.6	7.5	7.4	0.1	10.3	9.3	52.6	38.1	–
231 coffee, instant	1 tsp	2	3.4	100	419	14.6	11.0	4.5	6.5	0.0	–	–	–	0
232 cola	1 can	330	89.8	39	163	0.0	10.5	0.0	10.5	0.0	–	–	–	0
233 coleslaw		30	–	84	352	2.4	9.7	–	–	4.0	15.4	27.9	56.7	4
234 coley (saithe)		100	80.2	82	343	18.3	0.0	0.0	0.0	1.0	14.3	42.9	42.9	40
235 conger eel		225	73.2	114	477	18.1	0.0	0.0	0.0	4.6	–	–	–	–
236 coriander leaves		10	92.8	20	84	2.4	1.8	0.3	1.5	0.6	–	–	–	0
237 corn flakes breakfast cereal		20	3.0	355	1486	7.9	84.9	77.7	7.2	0.6	20.0	20.0	60.0	0
238 corn on the cob (sweetcorn, maize)	1 cob	210	41.2	66	276	2.5	11.6	10.0	1.4	1.4	20.0	30.0	50.0	0
239 corn snacks		30	3.3	519	2173	7.0	54.3	49.7	4.6	31.9	38.7	42.3	19.0	0
240 corned beef (canned)	1 thick slice	50	58.5	217	908	26.9	0.0	0.0	0.0	12.1	55.3	42.1	2.6	93
241 cornflour		–	12.5	354	1482	0.6	92.0	92.0	0.0	0.7	20.0	20.0	60.0	0
242 Cornish pastie		145	39.2	332	1390	8.0	31.1	29.9	1.2	20.4	38.1	54.1	7.7	49
243 courgette		100	93.0	19	80	2.0	2.0	0.1	1.9	0.4	–	–	–	0
244 couscous		150	40.0	227	950	5.7	51.3	–	–	1.0	–	–	–	–
245 crab, boiled, weighed w shell	1/2 dressed crab	325	14.5	25	105	4.0	0.0	0.0	0.0	1.0	14.3	42.9	42.9	11
246 crab, canned		85	79.2	341	1427	18.1	81.0	0.0	0.0	0.9	14.3	42.9	42.9	72
247 crabsticks	3 sticks	50	76.6	68	285	10.0	6.6	6.6	0.0	0.4	–	–	–	39
248 cranberries		80	87.0	15	63	0.4	3.4	0.0	3.4	0.1	–	–	–	0
249 crayfish		40	83.8	67	280	14.9	0.0	0.0	0.0	0.8	16.7	33.3	50.0	105
250 cream, clotted		25	32.2	586	2453	1.6	2.3	0.0	2.3	63.5	66.3	30.7	3.0	170
251 cream, double	1 tablespoon	30	47.5	449	1880	1.7	2.7	0.0	2.7	48.0	66.2	30.7	3.1	130
252 cream, half	individual portion	15	78.9	148	620	3.0	4.3	0.0	4.3	13.3	65.9	31.0	3.2	40
253 cream, single	1 tablespoon	15	73.7	198	829	2.6	4.1	0.0	4.1	19.1	66.5	30.7	2.8	55
254 cream, soured	small pot	60	72.5	205	858	2.9	3.8	0.0	3.8	19.9	66.1	30.7	3.2	60
255 cream, whipping	1 tablespoon	30	55.4	373	1561	2.0	3.1	0.0	3.1	39.3	66.3	30.7	3.0	105
256 creme caramel		100	72.0	109	456	3.0	20.6	2.6	18.0	2.2	–	–	–	–

per 100 g	fibre	non-starch polysaccharide	vit A	carotene	vit E	vit B₁	vit B₂	niacin	vit B₆	folate	vit C	sodium	calcium	iron	iodine
	g	g	µg	µg	mg	mg	mg	mg	mg	µg	mg	mg	mg	mg	µg
224 Coco Pops	1.1	0.6	0	0	-	1.00	1.50	17.2	1.80	250	0	880	35	6.7	–
225 cocoa powder	–	12.1	7	40	0.7	0.16	0.06	5.6	0.07	38	0	950	130	10.5	–
226 coconut	12.2	7.3	0	0	0.7	0.04	0.01	1.1	0.05	26	3	17	13	2.1	1
227 coconut, desiccated	21.1	13.7	0	0	1.3	0.03	0.05	2.0	0.09	9	0	28	23	3.6	3
228 cod	0.0	0.0	2	0	0.4	0.04	0.05	5.8	0.18	12	0	60	9	0.1	110
229 cod roe, battered, fried	0.3	0.2	–	–	–	0.09	0.22	2.9	0.08	22	0	510	67	1.4	–
230 cod, battered, fried	0.3	0.3	–	0	0.0	–	0.20	2.2	3.70	–	0	100	80	0.5	–
231 coffee, instant	0.0	0.0	0	0	–	0.00	0.11	24.9	0.03	0	0	41	160	4.4	0
232 cola	0.0	0.0	0	0	0.0	0.00	0.00	0.0	0.00	0	0	8	4	0.0	0
233 coleslaw	0.0	0.0	57	180	1.8	0.03	0.01	0.1	0.08	31	2	270	35	1.8	–
234 coley (saithe)	0.0	0.0	4	0	0.4	0.15	0.20	5.7	0.29	–	0	86	9	0.3	36
235 conger eel	0.0	0.0	–	0	–	0.06	0.04	7.7	–	–	0	50	71	1.3	–
236 coriander leaves	–	–	102	610	–	0.07	0.12	1.1	0.18	18	63	28	98	1.9	–
237 corn flakes breakfast cereal	3.4	0.9	0	0	0.4	1.00	1.50	16.9	1.80	250	0	1110	15	6.7	10
238 corn on the cob (sweetcorn, maize)	2.5	1.3	12	71	0.5	0.11	0.03	1.5	0.09	20	4	1	2	0.3	–
239 corn snacks	–	1.0	77	460	5.9	0.19	0.16	1.6	0.13	-	0	1130	68	0.8	–
240 corned beef (canned)	0.0	0.0	0	0	0.8	0.00	0.23	9.0	0.06	2	0	950	14	2.9	14
241 cornflour		0.1	0	0	0.0	0.00	0.00	0.1	0.00	0	0	52	15	1.4	
242 Cornish pastie	1.2	0.9	0	0	1.3	0.10	0.06	3.3	0.12	3	0	590	60	1.5	3
243 courgette	–	1.2	73	440	–	0.08	0.02	0.5	0.09	31	11	1	19	0.6	–
244 couscous	–	–	–	–	–	0.20	0.06	1.9	–	–	0	–	19	5.0	–
245 crab, boiled, weighed w shell	0.0	0.0	0	0	–	0.02	0.03	1.3	0.07	4	0	73	6	0.3	–
246 crab, canned	0.0	0.0	0	0	–	0.00	0.05	4.5	–	–	0	550	120	2.8	–
247 crabsticks	0.0	0.0	0	0	–	0.01	0.06	2.1	0.02	–	0	700	13	0.8	–
248 cranberries	3.8	3.0	4	22	–	0.03	0.02	0.2	0.07	2	13	2	12	0.7	–
249 crayfish	0.0	0.0	0	0	–	0.05	0.04	4.7	0.07	30	0	150	33	2.2	100
250 cream, clotted	0.0	0.0	819	685	1.5	0.02	0.16	0.4	0.03	6	0	18	37	0.1	0
251 cream, double	0.0	0.0	654	325	1.1	0.02	0.16	0.4	0.03	7	1	37	50	0.2	0
252 cream, half	0.0	0.0	199	54	0.3	0.03	0.18	0.8	0.05	6	1	49	99	0.1	–
253 cream, single	0.0	0.0	336	125	0.4	0.04	0.17	0.7	0.05	7	1	49	91	0.1	–
254 cream, soured	0.0	0.0	348	105	0.4	0.03	0.17	0.8	0.04	12	0	41	93	0.4	–
255 cream, whipping	0.0	0.0	609	265	0.9	0.02	0.17	0.5	0.04	7	1	40	62	0.0	–
256 creme caramel	–	–	38	8	0.2	0.03	0.20	0.8	0.03	8	0	70	94	0.0	33

per 100 g		average serving	water	energy	energy	protein	carbohydrates	starch	sugars	fat	saturated	mono-unsaturated	poly-unsaturated	cholesterol
		g	g	kcal	kJ	g	g	g	g	g	%	%	%	mg
257 creme eggs (Easter eggs)		39	5.3	385	1612	4.1	58.0	0.0	58.0	16.8	–	–	–	–
258 crispbread, rye	1	10	6.4	321	1344	9.4	70.6	67.4	3.2	2.1	20.0	20.0	60.0	0
259 crumpet	1	40	46.5	199	833	6.7	43.4	41.5	1.9	1.0	14.3	14.3	71.4	0
260 Crunchy Nut Corn Flakes		20	3.0	398	1666	7.4	88.6	52.3	36.3	4.0	21.1	47.4	31.6	0
261 cucumber		23	96.4	10	42	0.7	1.5	0.1	1.4	0.1	–	–	–	0
262 currants, dried	1 tablespooon	30	15.7	267	1118	2.3	67.8	0.0	67.8	0.4	–	–	–	0
263 custard apple (bullock's heart)	100		75.8	70	293	1.5	16.1	1.2	14.9	0.4	–	–	–	0
264 custard apple (sugar apple, sweetsop)	100		73.2	69	289	1.6	16.1	1.2	14.9	0.3	–	–	–	0
265 custard powder	1 tablespoon	30	12.5	354	1482	0.6	92.0	92.0	0.0	0.7	20.0	20.0	60.0	0
266 custard, made with egg		120	77.0	118	494	5.7	11.0	0.0	11.0	6.0	55.4	37.5	7.1	90
267 custard, made with milk from powder		120	75.5	117	490	3.7	16.6	5.1	11.4	4.5	65.1	30.2	4.7	16
268 dab		250	79.1	74	310	15.7	0.0	0.0	0.0	1.2	–	–	–	–
269 dahl, boiled		120	66.8	118	494	8.7	21.2	20.3	0.6	0.5	79.2	16.7	4.2	0
270 damsons		80	69.7	34	142	0.5	8.6	0.0	8.6	0.0	–	–	–	0
271 dates, dried	6 dates	90	12.3	227	950	2.8	57.1	0.0	57.1	0.2	–	–	–	0
272 dates, fresh	6 dates	150	52.2	107	448	1.3	26.9	0.0	26.9	0.1	–	–	–	0
273 dill leaves		5	83.9	25	105	3.7	0.9	0.1	0.8	0.8	–	–	–	0
274 dogfish (rock salmon)		150	68.3	154	645	16.6	0.0	0.0	0.0	9.7	20.9	38.8	40.3	76
275 dogfish (rock salmon), battered, fried		200	49.9	244	1021	15.4	7.1	7.0	0.1	17.3	–	–	–	0
276 doughnut, jam	1	75	26.9	336	1406	5.7	48.8	30.0	18.8	14.5	32.3	40.6	27.1	15
277 doughnut, ring	1	60	23.8	397	1662	6.1	47.2	31.9	15.3	21.7	31.3	41.3	27.4	24
278 Dover sole		250	80.0	89	373	18.1	0.0	0.0	0.0	1.8	–	–	–	50
279 drinking chocolate powder	for 1 mug	18	2.1	366	1532	5.5	77.4	3.6	73.8	6.0	61.4	35.1	3.5	0
280 dripping, beef		–	1.0	891	3730	0.0	0.0	0.0	0.0	99.0	58.3	39.0	2.7	94
281 drop scones (Scotch pancakes)	30		39.1	292	1222	5.8	43.6	34.8	8.9	11.7	36.6	39.3	24.1	61
282 duck, roast, meat only		185	64.2	189	791	25.3	0.0	0.0	0.0	9.7	29.3	57.6	13.0	160
283 duck, roast, meat, fat and skin	185		49.6	339	1419	19.6	0.0	0.0	0.0	29.0	29.2	57.9	12.9	–
284 dumplings, suet		70	60.5	208	871	2.8	24.5	24.0	0.4	11.7	58.4	39.1	2.6	82
285 durian		100	62.9	136	569	2.4	28.4	5.2	23.2	1.4	–	–	–	0
286 eel (weighed with bones)		225	71.3	168	703	16.6	0.0	0.0	0.0	11.3	29.3	54.5	16.2	150
287 eel, jellied		115	82.7	98	410	8.4	0.0	0.0	0.0	7.1	29.7	54.7	15.6	79

per 100 g	fibre	non-starch polysaccharide	vit A	carotene	vit E	vit B₁	vit B₂	niacin	vit B₆	folate	vit C	sodium	calcium	iron	iodine
	g	g	µg	µg	mg	mg	mg	mg	mg	µg	mg	mg	mg	mg	µg
257 creme eggs (Easter eggs)	0.0	0.0	56	55	1.1	0.06	0.34	1.5	0.03	12	0	55	120	0.8	–
258 crispbread, rye	11.6	11.7	0	0	0.5	0.28	0.14	2.9	0.29	35	0	220	45	3.5	15
259 crumpet	2.9	2.0	0	0	0.2	0.17	0.03	2.4	0.06	9	0	810	120	1.1	1
260 Crunchy Nut Corn Flakes	1.6	0.8	0	0	–	1.00	1.50	16.8	1.80	250	–	770	18	6.7	–
261 cucumber	0.7	0.6	10	60	0.1	0.03	0.01	0.3	0.04	9	2	3	18	0.3	3
262 currants, dried	5.9	1.9	1	6	–	0.16	0.05	1.1	0.23	4	0	14	93	1.3	–
263 custard apple (bullock's heart)	–	–	5	29	–	0.09	0.08	0.6	0.22	–	21	5	24	0.6	–
264 custard apple (sugar apple, sweetsop)	–	–	1	4	–	0.11	0.11	0.9	0.20	–	36	7	21	0.6	–
265 custard powder	–	0.1	0	0	0.0	0.00	0.00	0.1	0.00	0	0	320	15	1.4	–
266 custard, made with egg	0.0	0.0	93	21	0.2	0.05	0.24	1.6	0.08	12	0	82	130	0.4	25
267 custard, made with milk from powder	0.0	0.0	63	24	0.1	0.04	0.18	1.0	0.06	5	1	81	130	0.1	–
268 dab	0.0	0.0	–	0	0.4	0.10	0.08	5.2	0.19	5	0	77	24	0.3	30
269 dahl, boiled	4.1	–	2	11	–	0.15	0.04	1.4	–	25	0	14	14	1.0	–
270 damsons	3.3	1.6	44	265	0.6	0.09	0.03	0.4	0.05	3	5	2	22	0.4	–
271 dates, dried	6.5	3.4	6	34	–	0.06	0.08	2.8	0.16	11	0	8	38	1.1	–
272 dates, fresh	3.1	1.5	3	15	–	0.05	0.06	1.2	0.10	21	12	6	21	0.3	–
273 dill leaves	–	2.5	1017	6100	1.7	0.18	0.58	2.1	–	36	86	26	340	3.2	–
274 dogfish (rock salmon)	0.0	0.0	190	0	–	0.17	0.29	6.0	0.37	3	0	120	8	0.9	–
275 dogfish (rock salmon), battered, fried	0.3	0.3	86	0	1.9	0.06	0.09	–	–	–	0	270	39	1.0	–
276 doughnut, jam	2.5	–	–	–	0.0	0.22	0.07	2.5	0.03	21	–	180	72	1.2	15
277 doughnut, ring	3.1	–	–	–	0.0	0.22	0.07	2.4	0.02	19	0	230	76	1.2	17
278 Dover sole	0.0	0.0	0	0	–	0.06	0.10	6.4	–	–	0	100	29	0.8	–
279 drinking chocolate powder	–	–	–	–	0.2	0.06	0.04	1.7	0.02	10	0	250	33	2.4	–
280 dripping, beef	0.0	0.0	–	–	0.3	0.00	0.00	0.0	0.00	0	0	5	1	0.2	5
281 drop scones (Scotch pancakes)	1.6	1.4	120	–	1.1	0.13	0.09	2.0	0.08	6	0	430	120	1.0	18
282 duck, roast, meat only	0.0	0.0	–	–	0.0	0.26	0.47	10.5	0.25	10	0	96	13	2.7	–
283 duck, roast, meat, fat and skin	0.0	0.0	–	–	–	0.18	–	8.0	0.31	–	0	76	12	2.7	–
284 dumplings, suet	1.0	0.9	9	–	0.1	0.05	0.01	0.9	0.03	3	0	400	52	0.6	4
285 durian	4.0	–	2	11	–	0.29	0.29	1.1	–	–	41	1	14	0.9	–
286 eel (weighed with bones)	0.0	0.0	1200	0	4.1	0.20	0.35	5.4	0.25	12	0	89	19	1.2	80
287 eel, jellied	0.0	0.0	110	0	2.6	0.07	0.16	2.4	0.03	–	0	660	62	0.1	14

47

per 100 g		average serving	water	energy	energy	protein	carbohydrates	starch	sugars	fat	saturated	mono-unsaturated	poly-unsaturated	cholesterol
		g	g	kcal	kJ	g	g	g	g	g	%	%	%	mg
288 egg	large (size 1)	67	75.1	147	615	12.5	0.0	0.0	0.0	10.8	34.4	52.2	13.3	385
289 egg white	1 egg	32	88.3	36	151	9.0	0.0	0.0	0.0	0.0	–	–	–	0
290 egg yolk	1 egg	18	51.0	339	1419	16.1	0.0	0.0	0.0	30.5	34.4	52.2	13.4	1120
291 egg, duck		75	70.6	163	682	14.3	0.0	0.0	0.0	11.8	29.6	50.0	20.4	680
292 endive		20	93.7	13	54	1.8	1.0	0.0	1.0	0.2	–	–	–	0
293 faggots		150	47.1	268	1122	11.1	15.3	15.3	0.0	18.5	–	–	–	79
294 Farmhouse Bran breakfast cereal		30	4.0	303	1268	12.9	63.8	40.7	23.1	1.4	–	–	–	–
295 fat, cooking fat		–	0.0	894	3742	0.0	0.0	0.0	0.0	99.3	40.2	48.1	11.7	375
296 feijoa (pineapple guava)		–	85.0	47	197	0.9	10.3	0.3	10.0	0.5	–	–	–	0
297 fennel, Florence		100	94.4	11	46	0.9	1.5	0.1	1.4	0.2	–	–	–	0
298 figs, dried	1 fig	20	16.8	227	950	3.6	52.9	0.0	52.9	1.6	–	–	–	0
299 figs, fresh		55	84.6	43	180	1.3	9.5	0.0	9.5	0.3	–	–	–	0
300 fish cake fried with bun, takeaway		30	–	299	1250	9.6	27.0	–	–	16.9	24.2	47.4	28.4	70
301 fish cakes, fried		100	63.3	188	787	9.1	15.1	15.1	0.0	10.5	10.8	37.6	51.6	17
302 fish fingers, fried	3 fingers	85	55.6	233	975	13.5	17.2	17.2	0.0	12.7	23.3	45.0	31.7	–
303 fish fingers, grilled	3 fingers	85	56.2	214	896	15.1	19.3	19.3	0.0	9.0	32.9	40.0	27.1	35
304 fish paste	small jar	35	67.1	170	712	15.3	3.7	3.2	0.5	10.5	–	–	–	–
305 fish, average white fish		120	79.4	87	365	18.1	0.0	0.0	0.0	1.6	27.2	35.3	37.4	42
306 flounder		120	81.2	82	343	16.4	0.0	0.0	0.0	1.8	30.8	15.4	53.8	48
307 flour, chapati, white		–	12.0	335	1402	9.8	77.6	75.5	2.1	0.5	–	–	–	0
308 flour, chapati, brown		–	12.2	333	1394	11.5	73.7	70.5	3.2	1.2	25.0	12.5	62.5	0
309 flour, rye		–	15.0	335	1402	8.2	75.9	75.9	0.0	2.0	21.4	14.3	64.3	0
310 flour, wheat, brown		–	14.0	323	1352	12.6	68.5	66.8	1.7	1.8	16.7	16.7	66.7	0
311 flour, wheat, white, self raising	–	14.0	330	1381	8.9	75.6	74.3	1.3	1.2	25.0	12.5	62.5	0
312 flour, wheat, wholemeal		–	14.0	310	1298	12.7	63.9	61.8	2.1	2.2	18.8	18.8	62.5	0
313 flour, white, breadmaking		–	14.0	341	1427	11.5	75.3	73.9	1.4	1.4	22.2	11.1	66.7	0
314 flour, white, plain		–	14.0	341	1427	9.4	77.7	76.2	1.5	1.3	22.2	11.1	66.7	0
315 flying fish		120	77.5	86	360	21.0	0.0	0.0	0.0	0.3	–	–	–	–
316 frankfurters (see also hotdog)		120	59.5	274	1147	9.5	3.0	3.0	0.0	25.0	–	–	–	46
317 French dressing	1 tablespoon	15	22.8	649	2717	0.3	0.1	0.0	0.1	72.1	14.7	73.5	11.8	0
318 French fries, takeaway		110	43.8	280	1172	3.3	34.0	32.7	1.3	15.5	39.2	46.6	14.2	–
319 fromage frais, fruit	1 tablespoon	45	71.9	131	548	6.8	13.8	0.0	13.8	5.8	65.5	30.9	3.6	21

per 100 g	fibre	non-starch polysaccharide	vit A	carotene	vit E	vit B$_1$	vit B$_2$	niacin	vit B$_6$	folate	vit C	sodium	calcium	iron	iodine
	g	g	µg	µg	mg	mg	mg	mg	mg	µg	mg	mg	mg	mg	µg
288 egg	0.0	0.0	190	0	1.1	0.09	0.47	3.8	0.12	50	0	140	57	1.9	53
289 egg white	0.0	0.0	0	0	0.0	0.01	0.43	2.7	0.02	13	0	190	5	0.1	3
290 egg yolk	0.0	0.0	535	0	3.1	0.30	0.54	4.8	0.30	130	0	50	130	6.1	140
291 egg, duck	0.0	0.0	560	120	–	0.16	0.47	4.4	0.25	80	0	120	63	2.9	–
292 endive	2.0	2.0	73	440	–	0.06	0.10	0.6	0.02	140	12	10	44	2.8	–
293 faggots	0.5	–	470	60	–	0.14	0.49	5.1	0.17	22	0	820	55	8.3	–
294 Farmhouse Bran breakfast cereal	18.0	–	0	0	0.0	1.60	1.80	21.7	0.00	–	0	870	70	44.0	–
295 fat, cooking fat	0.0	0.0	0	0	0.0	0.00	0.00	0.0	0.00	0	0	0	0	0.0	0
296 feijoa (pineapple guava)	–	–	5	31	0.2	0.00	0.01	0.2	0.05	–	29	3	5	0.1	–
297 fennel, Florence	–	2.3	10	60	–	0.05	0.01	0.4	0.08	26	2	96	20	0.2	–
298 figs, dried	12.4	7.5	11	64	–	0.08	0.10	1.3	0.26	9	1	62	250	4.2	–
299 figs, fresh	2.3	1.5	25	150	–	0.03	0.03	0.6	0.08	–	2	3	38	0.3	–
300 fish cake fried with bun, takeaway	0.0	0.0	32	72	1.4	0.06	0.15	4.9	0.12	42	0	590	49	1.7	–
301 fish cakes, fried	0.6	–	0	0	–	0.06	0.06	2.8	–	–	0	500	70	1.0	–
302 fish fingers, fried	0.6	0.6	0	0	–	0.08	0.07	3.9	0.21	16	0	350	45	0.7	110
303 fish fingers, grilled	0.7	0.7	0	0	–	0.10	0.06	4.1	0.25	16	0	380	52	0.8	100
304 fish paste	0.2	0.2	19	0	0.9	0.02	0.20	7.0	–	–	0	600	280	9.0	310
305 fish, average white fish	0.0	0.0	3	0	0.4	0.08	0.12	6.5	0.35	9	0	85	31	0.6	80
306 flounder	0.0	0.0	–	0	0.4	0.14	0.21	6.5	0.25	11	0	92	27	0.4	25
307 flour, chapati, white	4.1		0	0	0.3	0.36	0.06	3.9	0.17	20	0	15	84	2.5	
308 flour, chapati, brown	10.3		0	0	0.6	0.26	0.05	6.2	0.29	29	0	39	86	3.4	
309 flour, rye		11.7	0	0	1.6	0.40	0.22	2.6	0.35	78	0	1	32	2.7	–
310 flour, wheat, brown	7.0	6.4	0	0	0.6	0.39	0.07	6.6	0.30	51	0	4	130	3.2	–
311 flour, wheat, white, self raising	4.1	3.1	0	0	0.3	0.30	0.03	3.3	0.15	19	0	360	350	2.0	10
312 flour, wheat, wholemeal	8.6	9.0	0	0	1.4	0.47	0.09	8.2	0.50	57	0	3	38	3.9	–
313 flour, white, breadmaking	3.7	3.1	0	0	0.3	0.32	0.03	4.3	0.15	31	0	3	140	2.1	–
314 flour, white, plain	3.6	3.1	0	0	0.3	0.31	0.03	3.6	0.15	22	0	3	140	2.0	10
315 flying fish	0.0	0.0	0	0	–	0.02	0.07	8.4	–	3	0	79	61	0.8	–
316 frankfurters (see also hotdog)	0.1	0.1	0	0	0.3	0.08	0.12	3.0	0.03	1	0	980	34	1.5	–
317 French dressing	0.0	0.0	0	2	3.6	0.00	0.00	0.0	0.00	0	0	930	12	0.3	1
318 French fries, takeaway	3.1	2.1	0	0	1.0	0.08	0.05	3.1	0.36	–	4	310	14	1.0	–
319 fromage frais, fruit	0.0	0.0	82	–	0.0	0.02	0.35	1.7	0.04	15	0	35	86	0.1	–

	per 100 g		average serving	water	energy	energy	protein	carbohydrates	starch	sugars	fat	saturated	mono-unsaturated	poly-unsaturated	cholesterol
			g	g	kcal	kJ	g	g	g	g	g	%	%	%	mg
320	fromage frais, plain	1 tablespoon	45	77.9	113	473	6.8	5.7	0.0	5.7	7.1	65.7	31.3	3.0	25
321	fromage frais, very low fat	1 tablespoon	45	83.7	58	243	7.7	6.8	0.0	6.8	0.2	–	–	–	1
322	Frosties breakfast cereal		20	3.0	382	1599	5.3	95.4	53.9	41.5	0.4	25.0	25.0	50.0	0
323	fruit cocktail, canned in juice		115	86.9	29	121	0.4	7.2	0.0	7.2	0.0	–	–	–	0
324	fruit cocktail, canned in syrup		115	81.8	57	239	0.4	14.8	0.0	14.8	0.0	–	–	–	0
325	fruit gums	each	2	12.0	172	720	1.0	44.8	2.2	42.6	0.0	–	–	–	0
326	fruit pie, individual		110	22.9	369	1545	4.3	56.7	25.8	30.9	15.5	–	–	–	–
327	Fruit'n Fibre		30	5.7	352	1473	8.1	73.1	46.4	26.7	5.1	52.1	27.1	20.8	0
328	gari (fermented cassava meal)	–		10.4	358	1499	1.3	92.9	91.9	1.0	0.5	–	–	0	
329	garlic		12	64.3	98	410	7.9	16.3	14.7	1.6	0.6	–	–	–	0
330	ghee		–	0.1	898	3759	0.0	0.0	0.0	0.0	99.8	70.6	25.8	3.6	280
331	ghee, palm		–	0.1	897	3755	0.0	0.0	0.0	0.0	99.7	51.5	38.7	9.8	0
332	ghee, vegetable		–	0.1	898	3759	0.0	0.0	0.0	0.0	99.8	–	–	–	0
333	goose, roast, meat only		150	46.7	319	1335	29.3	0.0	0.0	0.0	22.4	–	–	–	–
334	gooseberries, cooking		140	90.1	19	80	1.1	3.0	0.0	3.0	0.4	–	–	–	0
335	gooseberries, dessert		140	87.5	40	167	0.7	9.2	0.0	9.2	0.3	–	–	–	0
336	grape juice, unsweetened	1 glass	200	85.4	46	193	0.3	11.7	0.0	11.7	0.1	–	–	–	0
337	grapefruit	½ fruit	170	60.5	20	84	0.5	4.6	0.0	4.6	0.1	–	–	–	0
338	grapefruit juice, unsweetened	1 glass	200	89.4	33	138	0.4	8.3	0.0	8.3	0.1	–	–	–	0
339	grapefruit, canned in juice		120	88.6	30	126	0.6	7.3	0.0	7.3	0.0	–	–	–	0
340	grapefruit, canned in syrup		120	81.8	60	251	0.5	15.5	0.0	15.5	0.0	–	–	–	0
341	Grapenuts breakfast cereal		30	3.5	346	1448	10.5	79.9	67.8	12.1	0.5	–	–	–	–
342	grapes		100	77.7	57	239	0.4	14.6	0.0	14.6	0.1	–	–	–	0
343	greengages		80	77.9	38	159	0.7	9.2	0.0	9.2	0.1	–	–	–	0
344	grenadilla (yellow passion fruit)	100	74.7	42	176	2.8	7.5	0.0	7.5	0.3	–	–	–	0	
345	groundnuts (peanuts, monkey nuts)	10 whole nuts	13	6.3	564	2361	25.6	12.5	6.3	6.2	46.1	18.8	48.4	32.8	0
346	grouse, weighed with bone		350	40.6	114	477	20.6	0.0	0.0	0.0	3.5	24.2	12.1	63.6	–
347	guava		100	76.2	24	100	0.7	4.5	0.1	4.4	0.5	–	–	–	0
348	haddock		120	79.4	81	339	19.0	0.0	0.0	0.0	0.6	25.0	25.0	50.0	36
349	haggis		150	46.2	310	1298	10.7	19.2	19.2	0.0	21.7	47.8	43.4	8.8	91
350	hake		120	79.0	92	385	18.0	0.0	0.0	0.0	2.2	21.4	42.9	35.7	23
351	halibut		120	76.3	103	431	21.5	0.0	0.0	0.0	1.9	23.1	46.2	30.8	35

per 100 g	fibre	non-starch polysaccharide	vit A	carotene	vit E	vit B$_1$	vit B$_2$	niacin	vit B$_6$	folate	vit C	sodium	calcium	iron	iodine
	g	g	µg	µg	mg	mg	mg	mg	mg	µg	mg	mg	mg	mg	µg
320 fromage frais, plain	0.0	0.0	100	0	0.0	0.04	0.40	1.7	0.10	15	0	31	89	0.1	–
321 fromage frais, very low fat	0.0	0.0	3	–	0.0	0.03	0.37	1.9	0.07	15	0	33	87	0.1	–
322 Frosties breakfast cereal	1.2	0.5	0	0	–	1.00	1.50	16.6	1.80	250	0	740	11	6.7	–
323 fruit cocktail, canned in juice	1.0	1.0	9	54	–	0.01	0.01	0.4	0.04	6	14	3	9	0.4	–
324 fruit cocktail, canned in syrup	1.0	1.0	9	54	–	0.02	0.01	0.5	0.03	5	4	3	5	0.3	–
325 fruit gums	0.0	0.0	0	0	0.0	0.00	0.00	0.0	0.00	0	0	64	360	4.2	–
326 fruit pie, individual	2.3	–	0	0	–	0.05	0.02	1.3	–	–	–	210	51	1.2	–
327 Fruit'n Fibre	10.1	7.0	0	0	–	1.00	1.50	17.7	1.80	250	0	560	51	6.7	–
328 gari (fermented cassava meal)	2.9	–	0	0	0.1	0.03	1.00	0.3	0.00	–	7	–	37	3.1	–
329 garlic	–	4.1	0	0	0.0	0.13	0.03	2.2	0.38	5	17	4	19	1.9	3
330 ghee	0.0	0.0	758	500	3.3	0.00	0.00	0.0	0.00	0	0	2	0	0.2	–
331 ghee, palm	0.0	0.0	0	0	7.4	0.00	0.00	0.0	0.00	0	0	1	0	0.1	–
332 ghee, vegetable	0.0	0.0	0	0	10.3	0.00	0.00	0.0	0.00	0	0	1	0	0.0	–
333 goose, roast, meat only	0.0	0.0	–	–	–	0.12	0.51	10.1	0.42	12	0	150	10	4.6	–
334 gooseberries, cooking	2.9	2.4	18	110	0.4	0.03	0.03	0.5	0.02	8	14	2	28	0.3	0
335 gooseberries, dessert	3.1	2.4	10	62	0.4	0.03	0.03	0.4	0.02	8	26	1	19	0.6	0
336 grape juice, unsweetened	0.0	0.0	0	0	0.0	0.00	0.01	0.1	0.04	1	0	7	19	0.9	–
337 grapefruit	1.1	0.9	2	11	0.1	0.03	0.01	0.3	0.02	18	24	2	16	0.1	–
338 grapefruit juice, unsweetened	0.0	0.0	0	1	0.2	0.04	0.01	0.2	0.02	6	31	7	14	0.2	–
339 grapefruit, canned in juice	0.8	0.4	0	0	0.1	0.04	0.01	0.4	0.02	6	33	10	22	0.3	–
340 grapefruit, canned in syrup	0.9	0.6	0	0	0.1	0.04	0.01	0.3	0.02	4	30	10	17	0.7	–
341 Grapenuts breakfast cereal	6.2	–	1320	–	1.7	1.30	1.50	20.2	1.80	350	0	590	37	9.5	–
342 grapes	0.8	0.7	3	16	0.0	0.05	0.01	0.2	0.09	2	3	2	12	0.3	1
343 greengages	2.2	2.0	15	90	0.7	0.05	0.04	0.7	0.05	3	5	1	16	0.4	–
344 grenadilla (yellow passion fruit)	14.3	3.3	2	10	–	0.00	0.10	2.4	–	–	20	28	16	1.1	–
345 groundnuts (peanuts, monkey nuts)	7.3	6.2	0	0	10.1	1.14	0.10	19.3	0.59	110	0	2	60	2.5	20
346 grouse, weighed with bone	0.0	0.0	–	–	–	0.10	0.41	7.5	0.33	19	0	63	20	5.0	–
347 guava	4.2	3.3	65	390	–	0.04	0.04	1.0	0.13	–	210	5	12	0.4	–
348 haddock	0.0	0.0	0	0	0.4	0.04	0.07	8.0	0.39	9	0	67	14	0.1	250
349 haggis	–	–	1800	0	0.4	0.16	0.35	3.5	0.07	8	0	770	29	4.8	–
350 hake	0.0	0.0	–	0	–	–	–	–	–	–	0	100	14	0.5	–
351 halibut	0.0	0.0	–	0	0.9	0.07	0.07	9.8	0.38	9	0	60	29	0.5	40

per 100 g		average serving	water	energy	energy	protein	carbohydrates	starch	sugars	fat	saturated	mono-unsaturated	poly-unsaturated	cholesterol
		g	g	kcal	kJ	g	g	g	g	g	%	%	%	mg
352 ham and pork, chopped, canned	thick slice	45	58.5	275	1151	14.4	1.4	1.2	0.2	23.6	39.5	50.2	10.3	60
353 ham, canned	thick slice	45	72.5	120	502	18.4	0.0	0.0	0.0	5.1	41.3	45.7	13.0	68
354 hamburger, fried	quarter–pounder	90	53.0	264	1105	20.4	7.0	0.0	0.0	17.3	48.5	47.3	4.2	81
355 hazel nuts, shelled	10 nuts	10	4.6	650	2721	14.1	6.0	2.0	4.0	63.5	7.8	82.5	9.7	0
356 heart, lamb		200	75.6	119	498	17.1	0.0	0.0	0.0	5.6	48.8	39.5	11.6	140
357 heart, ox		200	76.3	108	452	18.9	0.0	0.0	0.0	3.6	63.0	33.3	3.7	140
358 heart, pig		200	79.2	93	389	17.1	0.0	0.0	0.0	2.7	–	–	–	–
359 herring		120	68.0	190	795	17.8	0.0	0.0	0.0	13.2	28.7	47.8	23.5	50
360 herring, grilled		120	44.5	135	565	13.9	0.0	0.0	0.0	8.8	31.6	50.6	17.7	34
361 herring, pickled		90	57.9	209	875	16.7	10.0	0.0	10.0	11.1	28.7	47.8	23.5	42
362 hoki		120	80.4	85	356	16.9	0.0	0.0	0.0	1.9	25.0	41.7	33.3	–
363 honey		20	23.0	288	1206	0.4	76.4	0.0	76.4	0.0	–	–	–	0
364 HoneySmacks breakfast cereal	20		3.0	371	1553	7.0	89.1	49.9	39.2	1.0	–	–	–	–
365 horseradish sauce	1 portion pack	20	64.0	153	640	2.5	17.9	3.0	14.9	8.4	13.6	46.9	39.5	14
366 hot dog, takeaway frankfurter and bun		30	–	275	1149	11.0	26.0	–	–	14.0	39.2	50.6	10.3	52
367 huckleberries		110	85.9	30	126	0.6	6.9	0.0	6.9	0.2	–	–	–	0
368 hummus		60	61.4	187	783	7.6	11.6	9.3	1.9	12.6	–	–	–	0
369 ice cream, choc ice		50	–	277	1160	3.5	28.1	–	–	17.5	64.7	28.7	6.6	7
370 ice cream, dairy		60	61.9	194	812	3.6	24.4	0.0	22.1	9.8	70.3	26.4	3.3	31
371 ice cream, non-dairy		60	65.3	178	745	3.2	23.1	0.0	19.2	8.7	52.4	38.1	9.5	7
372 ice cream, sorbet , water ice		60	64.9	131	548	0.9	34.2	0.0	34.2	0.0	–	–	–	0
373 Jaffa cakes	1 biscuit	13	18.0	363	1520	3.5	67.8	10.6	57.2	10.5	–	–	–	21
374 jam		15	29.8	261	1093	0.6	68.0	0.0	69.0	0.0	–	–	–	0
375 jam tarts	individual	35	14.4	368	1540	3.3	63.4	27.4	36.0	13.0	39.7	43.8	16.5	42
376 Japanese medlars (loquats)		–	88.5	28	117	0.7	6.3	0.0	6.3	0.2	–	–	–	0
377 jelly, packet		125	84.0	61	255	1.2	15.1	0.0	15.1	0.0	–	–	–	0
378 John Dory		120	78.1	89	373	19.0	0.0	0.0	0.0	1.4	30.0	20.0	50.0	–
379 jujube (Chinese date, Indian plum)	30		76.7	87	364	1.5	19.7	0.0	19.7	0.3	–	–	0	
380 kaki (sharon fruit, persimmon)		110	79.9	73	306	0.8	18.6	0.0	18.6	0.0	–	–	–	0
381 kale		95	90.9	24	100	2.4	1.0	0.1	0.9	1.1	22.2	11.1	66.7	0
382 KFC chicken hot wings		120	–	53	220	3.1	2.5	–	–	3.4	7.1	87.3	5.6	21
383 KFC chicken sandwich		165	–	290	1215	12.7	23.5	–	–	16.3	31.7	20.7	47.6	28

per 100 g	fibre	non-starch polysaccharide	vit A	carotene	vit E	vit B$_1$	vit B$_2$	niacin	vit B$_6$	folate	vit C	sodium	calcium	iron	iodine
	g	g	µg	µg	mg	mg	mg	mg	mg	µg	mg	mg	mg	mg	µg
352 ham and pork, chopped, canned	0.3	0.3	0	0	0.1	0.19	0.21	5.9	0.05	1	0	1090	14	1.2	20
353 ham, canned	0.0	0.0	0	0	0.1	0.52	0.25	6.9	0.22	0	0`	1250	9	1.2	11
354 hamburger, fried	0.0	0.0	0	0	0.6	0.02	0.23	8.0	0.20	15	0	880	33	3.1	0
355 hazel nuts, shelled	8.9	6.5	0	0	25.0	0.43	0.16	5.1	0.59	72	0	6	140	3.2	17
356 heart, lamb	0.0	0.0	0	0	0.4	0.48	0.90	10.5	0.29	2	7	140	7	3.6	–
357 heart, ox	0.0	0.0	0	0	0.5	0.45	0.80	10.3	0.23	4	7	95	5	4.9	–
358 heart, pig	0.0	0.0	0	0	0.4	0.48	0.90	10.6	0.29	2	5	80	6	4.8	–
359 herring	0.0	0.0	44	0	0.8	0.01	0.26	7.4	0.44	9	0	120	60	1.2	29
360 herring, grilled	0.0	0.0	23	0	0.2	0.00	0.12	5.3	0.39	7	0	120	22	0.7	21
361 herring, pickled	0.0	0.0	37	0	0.6	0.00	0.13	3.9	0.11	1	0	830	13	0.7	–
362 hoki	0.0	0.0	0	0	–	0.02	0.05	4.8	–	–	0	86	15	0.7	–
363 honey	0.0	0.0	0	0	0.0	0.00	0.05	0.2	–	–	0	11	5	0.4	–
364 HoneySmacks breakfast cereal	4.6	4.7	0	0	–	1.00	1.50	17.6	1.80	250	0	320	100	6.7	–
365 horseradish sauce	–	2.5	0	0	–	–	–	–	–	–	0	910	43	0.5	–
366 hot dog, takeaway frankfurter and bun	0.0	0.0	26	60	0.3	0.04	0.02	2.0	0.11	4	2	774	20	2.0	–
367 huckleberries	2.5	1.8	5	30	–	0.03	0.03	0.5	0.05	6	17	3	12	0.5	–
368 hummus	3.2	2.4	–	–	–	0.16	0.05	2.1	–	–	1	670	41	1.9	–
369 ice cream, choc ice	0.0	0.0	2	5	–	–	–	–	–	–	–	91	130	0.1	–
370 ice cream, dairy	0.0	0.0	148	195	0.2	0.04	0.25	0.9	0.08	7	1	69	130	0.1	–
371 ice cream, non-dairy	0.0	0.0	2	6	0.8	0.04	0.24	0.8	0.07	8	1	76	120	0.1	·
372 ice cream, sorbet, water ice	0.0	0.0	0	0	0.0	0.00	0.04	0.3	0.01	1	0	18	2	0.0	0
373 Jaffa cakes	–	–	14	0	0.8	0.05	0.05	1.0	0.03	5	2	130	55	1.5	48
374 jam	1.0	–	0	0	0.0	0.00	0.00	0.0	0.00	0	10	16	24	1.5	7
375 jam tarts	2.5	–	–	–	–	0.06	0.02	1.2	0.03	5	0	130	72	1.7	2
376 Japanese medlars (loquats)	–	–	86	515	–	0.02	0.03	0.2	–	–	3	1	20	0.4	–
377 jelly, packet	0.0	0.0	0	0	0.0	0.00	0.00	0.0	0.00	0	0	5	7	0.4	–
378 John Dory	0.0	0.0	0	0	–	–	–	3.6	0.95	–	0	60	40	–	–
379 jujube (Chinese date, Indian plum)	–	–	4	24	–	0.03	0.03	1.0	0.08	–	57	4	30	0.6	–
380 kaki (sharon fruit, persimmon)	–	1.6	158	950	–	0.03	0.05	0.3	–	7	19	5	10	0.1	–
381 kale	2.6	2.8	563	3375	1.3	0.02	0.06	1.3	0.13	86	71	100	150	2.0	–
382 KFC chicken hot wings	0.1	0.0	69	96	0.9	0.04	0.13	6.4	0.41	3	0	95	15	1.2	–
383 KFC chicken sandwich	0.8	0.0	8	0	1.7	0.24	0.21	8.1	0.35	18	0	639	60	1.9	–

per 100 g		average serving (g)	water (g)	energy (kcal)	energy (kJ)	protein (g)	carbohydrates (g)	starch (g)	sugars (g)	fat (g)	saturated (%)	mono-unsaturated (%)	poly-unsaturated (%)	cholesterol (mg)
384 KFC crispy chicken breast		135	–	253	1060	24.4	8.9	–	–	14.8	42.7	40.2	17.1	84
385 KFC crispy chicken drumstick		70	–	296	1238	20.3	8.7	–	–	20.3	34.4	42.7	22.9	103
386 KFC crispy chicken thigh		120	–	341	1428	16.8	11.8	–	–	25.2	42.2	36.7	21.1	108
387 KFC crispy chicken wing		65	–	391	1636	18.5	13.8	–	–	29.2	31.4	45.1	23.5	103
388 kidney, lamb	1 kidney	35	78.9	90	377	16.5	0.0	0.0	0.0	2.7	47.4	31.6	21.1	400
389 kidney, ox	1 portion	110	79.8	86	360	15.7	0.0	0.0	0.0	2.6	57.9	36.8	5.3	400
390 kidney, pig	1 kidney	140	78.8	90	377	16.3	0.0	0.0	0.0	2.7	45.0	35.0	20.0	410
391 kipper, boil in bag		170	60.7	237	992	20.0	0.0	0.0	0.0	17.4	–	–	–	–
392 kipper, grilled		130	35.2	161	674	12.7	0.0	0.0	0.0	12.2	18.0	57.7	24.3	44
393 Kit Kat	4 fingers	49	1.3	499	2089	8.2	60.5	13.7	46.8	26.6	55.0	38.6	6.4	–
394 kiwi (Chinese gooseberry)		60	72.2	42	176	1.0	9.1	0.3	8.9	0.4	–	–	–	0
395 kohl rabi		25	92.9	18	75	1.2	3.1	0.1	3.0	0.2	–	–	–	0
396 kumquats	4 fruits	30	83.4	43	180	0.9	9.3	0.0	9.3	0.5	–	–	–	0
397 ladies' fingers (bhindi, okra)		50	87.9	28	117	2.5	2.7	0.5	2.3	0.9	42.9	14.3	42.9	0
398 lamb, breast, roast		90	57.8	252	1055	25.6	0.0	0.0	0.0	16.6	53.0	41.6	5.4	110
399 lamb, cutlets, grilled		100	25.9	97	406	12.2	0.0	0.0	0.0	5.4	53.2	42.6	4.3	48
400 lamb, leg, roast		90	61.8	191	800	29.4	0.0	0.0	0.0	8.1	53.4	41.1	5.5	110
401 lamb, loin chops, grilled		120	32.4	122	511	15.3	0.0	0.0	0.0	6.8	53.3	41.7	5.0	48
402 lamb, scrag and neck, stewed		90	28.5	128	536	14.1	0.0	0.0	0.0	8.0	52.8	41.7	5.6	51
403 lamb, shoulder, roast		90	64.8	196	820	23.8	0.0	0.0	0.0	11.2	53.5	41.6	5.0	110
404 lard		–	1.0	891	3730	0.0	0.0	0.0	0.0	99.0	43.3	46.5	10.2	93
405 lasagne, boiled		230	75.7	100	419	3.0	22.0	21.5	0.5	0.6	–	–	–	–
406 lasagne, raw		30	9.7	346	1448	11.9	74.8	71.5	3.3	2.0	–	–	–	–
407 leeks		160	92.2	21	88	1.2	2.6	0.2	2.0	0.7	–	–	–	0
408 lemon		80	86.3	19	80	1.0	3.2	0.0	3.2	0.3	–	–	–	0
409 lemon curd		15	30.1	283	1185	0.6	62.7	22.3	40.4	5.1	–	–	–	0
410 lemon sole		170	81.2	83	347	17.4	0.0	0.0	0.0	1.5	20.0	30.0	50.0	60
411 lemon sole, goujons, fried		100	40.8	374	1566	15.5	14.3	13.4	0.9	28.7	–	–	–	–
412 lemonade	1 can	330	94.6	21	88	0.0	5.6	0.0	5.6	0.0	–	–	–	0
413 lentils, green, boiled		120	66.7	105	440	8.8	16.9	15.9	0.4	0.7	20.0	20.0	60.0	0
414 lentils, red, boiled		120	72.1	100	419	7.6	17.5	16.2	0.8	0.4	–	–	–	0
415 lettuce		20	95.1	14	59	0.8	1.7	0.0	1.7	0.5	–	–	–	0
416 lime		60	66.4	6	25	0.5	0.6	0.0	0.6	0.2	–	–	–	0

per 100 g	fibre	non-starch polysaccharide	vit A	carotene	vit E	vit B$_1$	vit B$_2$	niacin	vit B$_6$	folate	vit C	sodium	calcium	iron	iodine
	g	g	µg	µg	mg	mg	mg	mg	mg	µg	mg	mg	mg	mg	µg
384 KFC crispy chicken breast	0.1	0.0	15	0	0.5	0.08	0.13	13.6	0.57	4	0	585	16	1.2	–
385 KFC crispy chicken drumstick	0.1	0.0	25	0	0.9	0.08	0.22	6.0	0.34	8	0	470	12	1.3	–
386 KFC crispy chicken thigh	0.1	0.0	30	0	0.6	0.09	0.25	6.9	0.33	8	0	578	13	1.5	–
387 KFC crispy chicken wing	0.1	0.0	38	0	1.1	0.06	0.14	6.7	0.41	4	0	649	15	1.2	–
388 kidney, lamb	0.0	0.0	105	0	0.5	0.49	1.80	11.8	0.30	31	7	220	10	7.4	–
389 kidney, ox	0.0	0.0	96	0	0.2	0.37	2.10	9.4	0.32	77	10	180	10	5.7	15
390 kidney, pig	0.0	0.0	160	0	0.4	0.32	1.90	11.0	0.25	42	14	190	8	5.0	7
391 kipper, boil in bag	0.0	0.0	–	–	0.3	0.00	0.41	9.6	0.26	–	0	700	87	1.2	57
392 kipper, grilled	0.0	0.0	24	0	0.2	0.00	0.17	5.2	0.16	3	0	590	38	1.1	40
393 Kit Kat	–	–	8	47	1.0	0.11	0.44	3.1	0.06	–	0	110	200	1.5	–
394 kiwi (Chinese gooseberry)	–	1.6	5	32	–	0.01	0.03	0.6	0.13	–	51	3	21	0.3	–
395 kohl rabi	–	1.9	0	0	0.0	0.08	0.01	0.4	0.11	47	27	110	21	0.2	1
396 kumquats	–	3.8	29	175	–	0.07	0.07	0.6	–	–	39	6	25	0.6	–
397 ladies' fingers (bhindi, okra)	4.1	3.6	78	465	–	0.13	0.05	1.2	0.19	46	16	5	120	0.6	–
398 lamb, breast, roast	0.0	0.0	0	0	0.1	0.10	0.29	11.1	0.22	4	0	86	10	1.7	5
399 lamb, cutlets, grilled	0.0	0.0	0	0	0.0	0.07	0.13	5.8	0.10	2	0	33	4	0.9	2
400 lamb, leg, roast	0.0	0.0	0	0	0.1	0.14	0.38	12.9	0.22	4	0	67	8	2.7	5
401 lamb, loin chops, grilled	0.0	0.0	0	0	0.1	0.08	0.17	7.3	0.12	2	0	41	5	1.2	3
402 lamb, scrag and neck, stewed	0.0	0.0	0	0	0.1	0.03	0.11	4.6	0.11	2	0	130	5	1.2	3
403 lamb, shoulder, roast	0.0	0.0	0	0	0.1	0.10	0.27	9.4	0.22	4	0	65	9	1.8	5
404 lard	0.0	0.0	0	0	0.0	0.00	0.00	0.0	0.00	0	0	2	1	0.1	0
405 lasagne, boiled	1.4	0.9	0	0	0.0	0.05	0.01	1.0	0.01	6	0	1	6	0.5	0
406 lasagne, raw	4.9	3.1	0	0	0.0	0.49	0.06	4.9	0.11	37	0	10	23	1.8	0
407 leeks	2.4	1.7	96	575	0.8	0.02	0.02	0.6	0.10	40	7	6	20	0.7	–
408 lemon	4.7	–	3	18	–	0.05	0.04	0.3	0.11	–	58	5	85	0.5	–
409 lemon curd	0.2	0.2	10	0	0.0	0.00	0.02	0.1	0.00	0	0	65	9	0.5	–
410 lemon sole	0.0	0.0	0	0	–	0.09	0.08	3.7	–	11	0	95	17	0.5	–
411 lemon sole, goujons, fried	0.9	–	–	–	6.5	0.09	0.08	5.2	–	14	0	190	48	0.9	–
412 lemonade	0.0	0.0	0	0	0.0	0.00	0.00	0.0	0.00	0	0	7	5	0.0	0
413 lentils, green, boiled	–	3.8	–	–	–	0.14	0.08	1.8	0.28	30	0	3	22	3.5	–
414 lentils, red, boiled	3.3	1.9	3	20	–	0.11	0.04	1.4	0.11	5	0	12	16	2.4	–
415 lettuce	1.3	0.9	59	355	0.6	0.12	0.02	0.5	0.04	55	5	3	28	0.7	2
416 lime	–	–	2	9	–	0.02	0.01	0.2	0.06	6	34	1	17	0.3	–

per 100 g		average serving	water	energy	energy	protein	carbohydrates	starch	sugars	fat	saturated	mono-unsaturated	poly-unsaturated	cholesterol
		g	g	kcal	kJ	g	g	g	g	g	%	%	%	mg
417 ling		120	79.3	82	343	18.8	0.0	0.0	0.0	0.7	–	–	–	–
418 liqueurs		25	45.3	283	1185	0.0	30.5	0.0	30.5	0.0	–	–	–	0
419 liquorice allsorts	each	5	6.6	313	1310	3.9	74.1	6.9	67.2	2.2	33.3	27.8	38.9	0
420 liver paté		80	50.6	316	1323	13.1	1.0	0.7	0.3	28.9	39.6	47.6	12.7	169
421 liver paté, low fat		80	65.0	191	800	18.0	2.8	1.7	1.1	12.0	39.2	44.1	16.7	159
422 liver sausage		40	51.8	310	1298	12.9	4.3	3.5	0.8	26.9	39.7	42.7	17.6	184
423 liver, calf		100	69.7	153	640	20.1	1.9	1.9	0.0	7.3	40.7	24.1	35.2	370
424 liver, chicken		100	72.9	135	565	19.1	0.6	0.6	0.0	6.3	42.6	29.8	27.7	380
425 liver, lamb		100	67.3	179	749	20.1	1.6	1.6	0.0	10.3	39.2	40.5	20.3	430
426 liver, ox		100	68.6	163	682	21.1	2.2	2.2	0.0	7.8	50.0	22.4	27.6	270
427 liver, pork		100	69.5	154	645	21.3	2.1	2.1	0.0	6.8	42.9	20.4	36.7	260
428 lobster, boiled	1/4 dressed lobster	250	26.1	42	176	7.9	0.0	0.0	0.0	1.2	–	–	–	43
429 loganberries		80	85.0	17	71	1.1	3.4	0.0	3.4	0.0	–	–	–	0
430 loquats (Japanese medlars)		–	88.5	28	117	0.7	6.3	0.0	6.3	0.2	–	–	–	0
431 luncheon meat, canned	thick slice	20	51.5	313	1310	12.6	5.5	5.5	0.0	26.9	38.4	48.6	12.9	73
432 lychees	4 fruits	95	50.3	36	151	0.5	8.9	0.0	8.9	0.1	–	–	–	0
433 M and Ms, Smarties,	tube	37	1.5	456	1909	5.4	73.9	3.1	70.8	17.5	62.4	33.9	3.6	17
434 macadamia nuts (Queensland nuts)	6 nuts	10	1.3	748	3131	7.9	4.8	0.8	4.0	77.6	15.2	82.6	2.2	0
435 macaroni cheese		210	67.1	178	745	7.3	13.6	10.7	2.9	10.8	54.9	33.3	11.8	28
436 macaroni, boiled		230	78.1	86	360	3.0	18.5	18.2	0.3	0.5	25.0	8.3	66.7	0
437 macaroni, raw		30	9.7	348	1457	12.0	75.8	73.6	2.2	1.8	25.0	8.3	66.7	0
438 mackerel		160	64.0	220	921	18.7	0.0	0.0	0.0	16.1	22.8	54.5	22.8	54
439 mackerel, canned in brine		125	60.5	237	992	19.0	0.0	0.0	0.0	17.9	26.0	44.2	29.9	60
440 mackerel, canned in tomato		125	67.9	206	862	16.4	1.4	0.0	1.4	15.0	25.8	44.5	29.7	56
441 mackerel, grilled		160	53.9	220	921	19.1	0.0	0.0	0.0	15.9	23.1	54.5	22.4	53
442 mackerel, smoked		150	47.1	354	1482	18.9	0.0	0.0	0.0	30.9	22.7	54.5	22.7	104
443 maize (sweetcorn)	1 cob	210	41.2	66	276	2.5	11.6	10.0	1.4	1.4	20.0	30.0	50.0	0
444 mammie apple (mamey)		100	86.4	60	251	0.5	14.4	0.0	14.4	0.4	–	–	–	0
445 mange-tout, boiled		70	89.2	26	109	3.2	3.3	0.5	2.8	0.1	–	–	–	0
446 mango	1/2 fruit	110	56.0	39	163	0.5	9.6	0.2	9.4	0.1	–	–	–	0
447 mangosteen		–	81.0	73	306	0.6	16.4	0.3	16.1	0.5	–	–	–	0
448 margarine, dairy spread		15	22.0	662	2771	0.4	0.0	0.0	0.0	73.4	40.5	43.1	16.3	105
449 margarine, hard		15	16.0	739	3093	0.2	1.0	0.0	1.0	81.6	39.1	47.0	13.9	285

	fibre	non-starch polysaccharide	vit A	carotene	vit E	vit B₁	vit B₂	niacin	vit B₆	folate	vit C	sodium	calcium	iron	iodine
per 100 g	g	g	µg	µg	mg	mg	mg	mg	mg	µg	mg	mg	mg	mg	µg
417 ling	0.0	0.0	0	0	0.3	0.11	0.08	5.8	0.30	–	0	120	25	0.7	–
418 liqueurs	0.0	0.0	0	0	0.0	0.00	0.00	0.0	0.00	0	0	–	–	–	–
419 liquorice allsorts	–	–	0	0	0.0	0.00	0.00	0.7	0.00	0	0	75	63	8.1	–
420 liver paté	0.0	0.0	7352	130	–	0.13	1.10	5.7	0.25	89	–	790	15	7.1	–
421 liver paté, low fat	0.0	0.0	5925	0	0.8	0.46	1.12	10.7	0.35	–	18	710	14	6.3	–
422 liver sausage	0.5	0.5	2605	0	0.1	0.17	1.58	6.7	0.14	19	0	860	26	6.4	–
423 liver, calf	0.0	0.0	29747	100	0.2	0.21	3.10	16.7	0.54	240	18	93	7	8.0	–
424 liver, chicken	0.0	0.0	11325	0	0.3	0.36	2.70	14.3	0.40	590	23	85	8	9.5	–
425 liver, lamb	0.0	0.0	19905	60	0.5	0.27	3.30	18.5	0.42	220	10	76	7	9.4	5
426 liver, ox	0.0	0.0	16757	1540	0.4	0.23	3.10	17.9	0.83	330	23	81	6	7.0	13
427 liver, pork	0.0	0.0	17595	0	0.2	0.31	3.00	19.4	0.68	110	13	87	6	21.0	–
428 lobster, boiled	0.0	0.0	0	0	0.5	0.03	0.02	2.0	–	6	0	120	22	0.3	–
429 loganberries	5.6	2.5	1	6	0.5	0.03	0.05	0.7	0.06	33	35	3	35	1.4	–
430 loquats (Japanese medlars)	–	–	86	515	–	0.02	0.03	0.2	–	–	3	1	20	0.4	–
431 luncheon meat, canned	0.4	0.3	0	0	0.1	0.07	0.12	4.5	0.02	1	0	1050	15	1.1	–
432 lychees	0.9	0.4	0	0	–	0.02	0.04	0.3	–	–	28	1	4	0.3	–
433 M and Ms, Smarties,	0.0	0.0	5	28	0.8	0.08	0.79	2.0	0.03	10	0	58	150	1.5	–
434 macadamia nuts (Queensland nuts)	–	5.3	0	0	1.5	0.28	0.06	3.3	0.28	–	0	–	47	1.6	–
435 macaroni cheese	0.8	0.5	122	74	0.5	0.04	0.16	2.0	0.05	5	0	310	170	0.4	16
436 macaroni, boiled	1.5	0.9	0	0	0.0	0.03	0.00	1.1	0.01	3	0	1	6	0.5	0
437 macaroni, raw	5.0	3.1	0	0	0.0	0.18	0.05	5.4	0.10	23	0	11	25	1.6	0
438 mackerel	0.0	0.0	45	0	0.4	0.14	0.29	12.1	0.41	–	0	63	11	0.8	140
439 mackerel, canned in brine	0.0	0.0	37	0	–	0.03	0.27	8.9	0.14	–	0	270	29	1.1	49
440 mackerel, canned in tomato	0.0	0.0	59	165	1.9	0.07	0.20	8.1	0.20	6	0	250	82	1.0	47
441 mackerel, grilled	0.0	0.0	44	0	0.4	0.14	0.29	12.2	0.41	–	0	58	11	0.7	150
442 mackerel, smoked	0.0	0.0	25	0	0.3	0.26	0.52	13.2	1.03	–	0	750	20	1.2	150
443 maize (sweetcorn)	2.5	1.3	12	71	0.5	0.11	0.03	1.5	0.09	20	4	1	2	0.3	–
444 mammie apple (mamey)	–	–	22	130	–	0.02	0.04	0.5	–	–	15	15	12	0.6	–
445 mange-tout, boiled	4.0	2.2	111	665	0.4	0.14	0.16	0.9	0.14	6	28	2	35	0.8	–
446 mango	2.0	1.8	204	1225	0.7	0.03	0.03	0.4	0.09	–	25	1	8	0.5	–
447 mangosteen	1.3	–	0	0	–	0.05	0.01	0.4	–	–	3	1	14	0.3	–
448 margarine, dairy spread	0.0	0.0	941	845	5.1	0.00	0.00	0.1	0.00	0	0	760	14	0.0	–
449 margarine, hard	0.0	0.0	790	750	–	0.00	0.00	0.0	0.00	0	0	800	4	0.3	23

per 100 g		average serving g	water g	energy kcal	energy kJ	protein g	carbohydrates g	starch g	sugars g	fat g	saturated %	mono-unsaturated %	poly-unsaturated %	cholesterol mg
450	margarine, hard, vegetarian	15	16.0	739	3093	0.2	1.0	0.0	1.0	81.6	45.8	42.1	12.0	15
451	margarine, low fat spread	15	49.9	390	1633	5.8	0.5	0.0	0.5	40.5	28.9	45.5	25.6	6
452	margarine, polyunsaturated	15	16.0	739	3093	0.2	1.0	0.0	1.0	81.6	20.8	26.4	52.8	7
453	margarine, soft	15	16.0	739	3093	0.2	1.0	0.0	1.0	81.6	34.5	47.8	17.7	225
454	margarine, soft, vegetarian	15	16.0	739	3093	0.2	1.0	0.0	1.0	81.6	32.1	39.8	28.0	9
455	margarine, very low fat spread	15	–	273	1143	8.3	3.6	0.0	3.6	25.0	27.7	57.4	14.9	–
456	marmalade	15	28.0	261	1093	0.1	69.5	0.0	69.5	0.0	–	–	–	0
457	Marmite	4	25.4	172	720	39.7	1.8	1.8	0.0	0.7	–	–	–	–
458	marrow	65	95.9	9	38	0.4	1.6	0.2	1.4	0.2	–	–	–	0
459	Mars bar	standard bar	65	6.9	441	1846	5.3	66.5	0.7	65.8	18.9	55.6	40.0	4.4	25
460	marzipan (almond paste)	–	7.9	404	1691	5.3	67.6	0.0	67.6	14.4	8.7	64.5	26.8	0
461	matoki (green banana)	200	74.1	91	381	1.3	22.3	21.7	0.6	0.2	–	–	–	0
462	matzo	1 piece	23	6.7	384	1607	10.5	86.6	82.4	4.2	1.9	–	–	–	–
463	mayonnaise, bought	20	18.8	691	2893	1.1	1.7	0.4	1.3	75.6	15.4	23.9	60.7	75
464	mayonnaise, home made	20	16.9	724	3031	1.9	0.2	0.0	0.1	79.3	15.5	73.1	11.4	120
465	mayonnaise, reduced calorie	20	59.6	288	1206	1.0	8.2	3.6	4.6	28.0	–	–	–	–
466	McDonalds apple bran muffin	85	–	224	936	5.9	54.1	–	–	0.0	–	–	–	0
467	McDonalds apple Danish	115	–	339	1420	5.0	44.5	–	–	15.6	21.5	66.5	12.1	22
468	McDonalds apple pie	80	–	313	1311	2.7	36.1	–	–	17.8	32.6	61.5	5.9	0
469	McDonalds bacon and egg biscuit	160	–	282	1181	11.2	21.3	–	–	16.9	31.2	61.1	7.6	162
470	McDonalds barbecue sauce	30	–	156	654	0.9	37.8	–	–	1.6	12.8	40.4	46.8	0
471	McDonalds Big Mac	215	–	260	1090	11.7	19.8	–	4.8	15.1	31.9	63.4	4.7	48
472	McDonalds Cheeseburger	120	–	267	1119	12.9	26.9	–	5.0	11.9	37.6	55.7	6.8	46
473	McDonalds Chef salad	280	–	81	340	7.2	2.7	–	–	4.7	44.3	48.9	6.8	45
474	McDonalds Chicken McNuggets	112	–	257	1074	16.8	14.6	–	–	14.4	25.2	63.9	10.9	58
475	McDonalds Chocolaty Cookie	56	–	589	2467	7.5	74.8	–	–	27.9	32.2	65.3	2.5	7
476	McDonalds Chunky Chicken salad	250	–	56	234	9.2	2.1	–	–	1.4	27.2	57.7	15.1	31
477	McDonalds croutons	10	–	455	1903	12.6	61.8	–	–	19.7	23.9	70.2	5.9	0
478	McDonalds Egg McMuffin	140	–	210	880	13.2	20.4	–	2.0	8.1	34.1	54.4	11.5	164
479	McDonalds English muffin	60	–	288	1206	9.2	45.3	–	–	7.8	52.2	36.8	11.0	15
480	McDonalds Filet o'Fish	140	–	310	1297	9.7	26.7	–	3.3	18.4	19.7	39.0	41.3	35
481	McDonalds Garden salad	210	–	52	216	3.3	2.9	–	–	3.1	44.0	48.0	8.0	39

per 100 g	fibre	non-starch polysaccharide	vit A	carotene	vit E	vit B₁	vit B₂	niacin	vit B₆	folate	vit C	sodium	calcium	iron	iodine
	g	g	µg	µg	mg	mg	mg	mg	mg	µg	mg	mg	mg	mg	µg
450 margarine, hard, vegetarian	0.0	0.0	790	750	–	0.00	0.00	0.0	0.00	0	0	800	4	0.3	23
451 margarine, low fat spread	0.0	0.0	1084	985	6.3	0.00	0.00	1.4	0.00	0	0	650	39	0.0	–
452 margarine, polyunsaturated	0.0	0.0	900	750	–	0.00	0.00	0.0	0.00	0	0	800	4	0.3	27
453 margarine, soft	0.0	0.0	985	750	–	0.00	0.00	0.0	0.00	0	0	800	4	0.3	27
454 margarine, soft, vegetarian	0.0	0.0	985	750	–	0.00	0.00	0.0	0.00	0	0	800	4	0.3	27
455 margarine, very low fat spread	0.0	0.0	–	–	–	0.00	0.00	1.9	0.00	0	0	1050	–	–	–
456 marmalade	0.6	0.6	8	50	0.0	0.00	0.00	0.0	0.00	5	10	18	35	0.6	7
457 Marmite	0.0	0.0	0	0	–	3.10	11.00	67.0	1.30	1010	0	4500	95	3.7	49
458 marrow	1.0	0.6	18	110	0.0	0.08	0.00	0.3	0.01	15	3	1	14	0.1	–
459 Mars bar	0.0	0.0	7	40	–	0.05	0.20	1.1	0.03	–	0	150	160	1.1	–
460 marzipan (almond paste)	3.2	1.9	0	0	6.2	0.05	0.19	1.6	0.04	12	0	20	66	0.9	0
461 matoki (green banana)	2.0	1.5	9	51	-	0.05	0.08	0.6	0.27	44	8	130	3	0.3	–
462 matzo	3.5	3.0	0	0	0.0	0.11	0.03	3.1	0.06	–	0	17	32	1.5	–
463 mayonnaise, bought	0.0	0.0	103	100	18.9	0.02	0.07	0.3	0.01	4	–	450	8	0.3	35
464 mayonnaise, home made	0.0	0.0	56	0	4.2	0.03	0.06	0.5	0.03	13	0	240	17	0.8	16
465 mayonnaise, reduced calorie	0.0	0.0	–	–	–	–	–	–	–	–	–	940	–	–	–
466 McDonalds apple bran muffin	5.3	0.0	1	0	0.5	0.02	0.09	0.5	0.44	90	1	271	36	0.7	–
467 McDonalds apple Danish	1.4	0.0	33	16	3.9	0.24	0.17	1.9	0.02	3	14	322	12	1.2	–
468 McDonalds apple pie	1.4	0.0	0	0	3.9	0.07	0.02	0.4	0.02	3	14	289	13	0.9	–
469 McDonalds bacon and egg biscuit	0.5	0.0	115	77	1.2	0.23	0.21	1.6	0.11	11	0	788	119	1.6	–
470 McDonalds barbecue sauce	5.9	0.0	268	1043	6.6	0.03	0.03	0.5	0.08	4	7	1063	40	1.0	–
471 McDonalds Big Mac	–	0.0	49	–	–	0.22	0.19	3.2	0.13	10	1	442	119	1.9	68
472 McDonalds Cheeseburger	–	0.0	102	–	0.5	0.25	0.18	3.3	0.10	16	2	647	172	2.0	–
473 McDonalds Chef salad	–	0.0	145	–	–	0.11	0.10	1.3	–	–	5	173	90	0.5	–
474 McDonalds Chicken McNuggets	–	0.0	0	0	–	0.10	0.11	7.9	–	–	0	460	11	0.9	–
475 McDonalds Chocolaty Cookie	2.0	0.0	0	0	3.1	0.32	0.38	4.4	0.05	9	0	500	43	3.9	–
476 McDonalds Chunky Chicken salad	0.4	0.0	152	34	5.2	0.09	0.07	3.4	0.24	11	8	92	14	0.4	–
477 McDonalds croutons	4.7	0.0	0	0	1.0	0.45	0.27	3.8	0.06	31	1	1273	59	3.2	–
478 McDonalds Egg McMuffin	1.0	0.0	121	72	1.5	0.34	0.24	2.7	0.12	32	1	536	186	2.0	–
479 McDonalds English muffin	2.6	0.0	62	0	0.3	0.56	0.24	4.2	0.16	87	0	458	256	2.7	–
480 McDonalds Filet o'Fish	0.8	0.0	31	–	–	0.21	0.11	1.9	0.07	14	0	725	116	1.3	108
481 McDonalds Garden salad	0.8	0.0	374	1144	0.5	0.05	0.08	0.3	0.23	27	6	75	70	0.6	–

per 100 g	average serving (g)	water (g)	energy (kcal)	energy (kJ)	protein (g)	carbohydrates (g)	starch (g)	sugars (g)	fat (g)	saturated (%)	mono-unsaturated (%)	poly-unsaturated (%)	cholesterol (mg)
482 McDonalds hamburger	100	–	255	1067	12.1	30.0	–	4.5	9.3	38.3	53.6	8.1	36
483 McDonalds hash brown potatoes	55	–	236	989	2.5	27.1	–	–	13.3	44.6	50.3	5.1	16
484 McDonalds honey sauce	14	–	321	1346	0.0	82.1	–	–	0.0	–	–	–	0
485 McDonalds hot cakes with syrup	175	–	233	975	4.7	42.3	–	–	5.2	39.7	33.6	26.7	12
486 McDonalds hot caramel sundae	175	–	155	650	3.8	34.1	–	–	1.6	53.5	43.3	3.2	7
487 McDonalds hot fudge sundae	170	–	142	594	4.3	29.9	–	–	1.9	74.4	24.1	1.6	4
488 McDonalds hot mustard sauce	30	–	233	977	1.7	27.3	–	–	12.0	14.2	34.2	51.7	17
489 McDonalds iced cheese Danish	110	–	355	1484	6.7	38.5	–	–	19.8	30.0	61.0	8.9	43
490 McDonalds McChicken sandwich	190	–	258	1080	10.1	20.9	–	–	15.1	18.9	40.4	40.7	22
491 McDonalds McDLT hamburger	230	–	248	1038	11.2	15.4	–	–	15.7	31.3	45.5	23.2	47
492 McDonalds McDonaldland Cookie	56	–	518	2168	7.5	84.1	–	–	16.4	20.2	74.2	5.7	0
493 McDonalds McLean deluxe hamburger	210	–	155	650	10.7	17.0	–	–	4.9	40.0	50.0	10.0	29
494 McDonalds milk shake, chocolate, low fat	290	–	109	457	4.1	22.5	–	–	0.7	50.0	50.0	0.0	3
495 McDonalds milk shake, strawberry, vanilla low fat	290	–	99	414	3.8	20.5	–	–	0.3	50.0	50.0	0.0	3
496 McDonalds pork sausage	50	–	375	1570	17.5	0.0	–	0.0	34.0	36.1	52.2	11.7	100
497 McDonalds Quarterpounder cheeseburger	190	–	268	1122	14.7	18.1	–	5.1	15.1	38.3	56.5	5.2	61
498 McDonalds Quarterpounder hamburger	165	–	247	1034	13.9	20.5	–	4.1	12.5	39.1	55.1	5.8	52
499 McDonalds raspberry Danish	115	–	350	1467	5.2	52.6	–	–	13.6	21.6	70.8	7.6	22
500 McDonalds salad dressing, peppercorn	28.4	–	563	2358	0.0	7.0	–	–	63.4	12.5	25.0	62.5	49
501 McDonalds salad dressing, red French	28.4	–	282	1179	0.0	35.2	–	–	14.1	0.0	50.0	50.0	0
502 McDonalds sausage and egg biscuit	180	–	289	1209	11.1	18.1	–	–	19.2	33.2	59.3	7.5	153
503 McDonalds sausage biscuit	120	–	358	1497	10.6	25.9	–	–	23.6	32.0	59.3	8.8	40
504 McDonalds sausage McMuffin with egg — medium	115	–	316	1324	14.1	23.3	–	–	18.7	35.5	53.4	11.1	55
505 McDonalds sausage McMuffin with egg — large	170	–	263	1103	13.5	16.7	–	–	16.0	35.3	53.0	11.8	157
506 McDonalds scrambled eggs	100	–	143	598	12.7	1.2	–	0.9	10.0	34.0	51.3	14.7	407
507 McDonalds side salad	115	–	52	218	3.2	2.9	–	–	2.9	43.8	48.0	8.2	36

	fibre	non-starch polysaccharide	vit A	carotene	vit E	vit B$_1$	vit B$_2$	niacin	vit B$_6$	folate	vit C	sodium	calcium	iron	iodine
per 100 g	g	g	µg	µg	mg	mg	mg	mg	mg	µg	mg	mg	mg	mg	µg
482 McDonalds hamburger	–	0.0	45	–	0.5	0.27	0.16	3.8	0.12	17	2	490	120	2.2	–
483 McDonalds hash brown potatoes	2.0	0.0	0	0	0.2	0.11	0.04	1.5	0.13	6	3	600	10	0.5	–
484 McDonalds honey sauce	–	0.0	0	0	–	0.00	0.07	0.3	–	–	1	0	–	0.5	–
485 McDonalds hot cakes with syrup	–	0.0	30	–	–	0.18	0.19	1.6	0.07	5	3	364	65	1.2	10
486 McDonalds hot caramel sundae	0.6	0.0	66	96	0.8	0.05	0.20	0.1	0.22	11	0	103	128	0.0	–
487 McDonalds hot fudge sundae	0.7	0.0	55	102	0.8	0.05	0.21	0.2	0.04	4	0	101	139	0.3	–
488 McDonalds hot mustard sauce	0.8	0.0	5	0	4.8	0.03	0.03	0.5	0.03	4	2	833	50	0.7	–
489 McDonalds iced cheese Danish	–	0.0	34	–	–	0.26	0.21	1.9	–	–	1	382	30	1.3	–
490 McDonalds McChicken sandwich	0.8	0.0	16	0	1.7	0.51	0.11	4.7	0.35	18	1	411	75	1.4	–
491 McDonalds McDLT hamburger	–	0.0	97	–	–	0.17	0.15	2.9	–	–	3	423	96	1.7	–
492 McDonalds McDonaldland Cookie	1.0	0.0	0	0	3.1	0.45	0.32	4.5	0.05	7	0	536	16	3.7	–
493 McDonalds McLean deluxe hamburger	1.2	0.0	91	355	1.6	0.17	0.15	2.8	0.12	23	5	325	45	1.8	–
494 McDonalds milk shake, chocolate, low fat	–	0.0	–	–	–	–	–	–	–	–	–	82	113	–	–
495 McDonalds milk shake, strawberry, vanilla low fat	0.0	0.0	15	12	0.0	0.04	0.20	0.1	0.05	11	1	58	112	0.1	–
496 McDonalds pork sausage	0.0	0.0	0	0	–	0.56	0.21	4.8	–	–	0	729	17	1.4	–
497 McDonalds Quarterpounder cheeseburger	–	0.0	109	–	–	0.19	0.20	3.5	0.12	12	2	593	152	1.9	–
498 McDonalds Quarterpounder hamburger	–	0.0	40	–	–	0.22	0.17	4.0	0.16	14	2	398	86	2.2	–
499 McDonalds raspberry Danish	–	0.0	30	–	–	0.28	0.18	1.8	–	–	3	265	12	1.3	–
500 McDonalds salad dressing, peppercorn	0.0	0.0	20	0	10.1	0.01	0.02	0.0	0.01	4	0	599	11	0.4	–
501 McDonalds salad dressing, red French	0.0	0.0	20	0	10.1	0.01	0.02	0.0	0.01	4	0	775	11	0.4	–
502 McDonalds sausage and egg biscuit	–	0.0	49	–	–	0.29	0.19	2.2	0.11	22	0	694	64	1.8	–
503 McDonalds sausage biscuit	1.1	0.0	0	0	3.0	0.40	0.17	3.2	0.09	7	0	878	68	1.6	–
504 McDonalds sausage McMuffin with egg	0.9	0.0	81	119	1.7	0.51	0.25	4.1	0.11	41	1	709	201	2.0	–
505 McDonalds sausage McMuffin with egg	0.9	0.0	110	119	1.7	0.38	0.25	2.9	0.11	41	0	587	157	2.0	–
506 McDonalds scrambled eggs	0.0	0.0	185	153	3.5	0.07	0.27	0.1	0.08	28	1	296	58	2.1	–
507 McDonalds side salad	1.1	0.0	227	231	0.4	0.04	0.07	0.3	0.05	35	6	74	66	0.6	–

per 100 g		average serving	water	energy	energy	protein	carbohydrates	starch	sugars	fat	saturated	mono-unsaturated	poly-unsaturated	cholesterol
		g	g	kcal	kJ	g	g	g	g	g	%	%	%	mg
508 McDonalds strawberry sundae	170	–	123	514	3.3	28.8	–	–	0.6	59.4	36.8	3.8	3	
509 McDonalds sweet and sour sauce	30	–	188	785	0.6	43.1	–	–	0.6	13.0	43.5	43.5	0	
510 McDonalds vanilla frozen yogurt	80	–	125	523	5.0	27.5	–	–	0.9	54.7	37.3	8.0	4	
511 medlars		60	74.5	42	176	0.5	10.6	0.0	10.6	0.0	–	–	–	0
512 melon seeds		15	6.1	583	2440	28.5	9.9	–	–	47.7	25.8	17.8	56.3	0
513 melon, canteloupe		230	60.8	13	54	0.4	2.8	0.0	2.8	0.1	–	–	–	0
514 melon, galia		230	63.4	16	67	0.3	3.8	0.0	3.8	0.1	–	–	–	0
515 melon, honeydew		310	59.9	19	80	0.4	4.3	0.0	4.3	0.1	–	–	–	0
516 melon, watermelon		200	92.3	31	130	0.5	7.1	0.0	7.1	0.3	–	–	–	0
517 meringue (unfilled)		8	2.2	379	1586	5.3	95.4	0.0	95.4	0.0	–	–	–	0
518 milk, calcium fortified	1 pint	585	88.2	40	167	4.0	5.7	0.0	5.7	0.3	66.7	30.6	2.8	4
519 milk, Channel Island	1 pint	585	86.4	78	327	3.6	4.8	0.0	4.8	5.1	70.2	27.7	2.1	16
520 milk, evaporated	1/2 small can	85	69.1	151	632	8.4	8.5	0.0	8.5	9.4	66.3	30.3	3.4	34
521 milk, full cream	1 pint	585	87.8	66	276	3.2	4.8	0.0	4.8	3.9	66.7	30.6	2.8	14
522 milk, goat	1 pint	585	88.9	60	251	3.1	4.4	0.0	4.4	3.5	71.9	25.0	3.1	10
523 milk, semi-skimmed	1 pint	585	89.8	46	193	3.3	5.0	0.0	5.0	1.6	66.7	30.6	2.8	7
524 milk, sheep	1 pint	585	83.0	95	398	5.4	5.1	0.0	5.1	6.0	67.9	26.8	5.4	11
525 milk, skimmed	1 pint	585	91.1	33	138	3.3	5.0	0.0	5.0	0.1	–	–	–	2
526 Milky Way	standard bar	26	6.6	397	1662	4.4	63.4	0.8	62.6	15.8	55.3	38.7	6.0	–
527 mincemeat (sweet)		25	27.5	274	1147	0.6	62.1	0.0	62.1	4.3	58.5	39.0	2.4	4
528 mint		5	86.4	43	180	3.8	5.3	–	–	0.7	–	–	–	0
529 mint sauce	2 teaspoons	10	68.7	87	364	1.6	21.5	0.0	21.5	0.0	–	–	–	0
530 monkey nuts (peanuts, groundnuts)	10 whole nuts	13	6.3	564	2361	25.6	12.5	6.3	6.2	46.1	18.8	48.4	32.8	0
531 monkfish		70	83.3	66	276	15.7	0.0	0.0	0.0	0.4	33.3	33.3	33.3	14
532 mooli (white radish)		30	93.0	15	63	0.8	2.9	0.0	2.9	0.1	–	–	–	0
533 muesli, no added sugar		30	6.7	366	1532	10.5	67.1	51.8	15.3	8.1	20.3	47.3	32.4	0
534 muesli, Swiss style		30	7.0	364	1524	10.6	71.1	47.4	23.7	5.9	15.4	53.8	30.8	0
535 muesli, with extra fruit		30	8.5	372	1557	10.2	73.4	51.1	22.3	6.2	–	–	–	–
536 muffins	1	70	33.9	283	1185	10.1	49.6	47.0	2.6	6.3	–	–	–	–
537 muffins, bran	1	72	30.1	272	1139	7.8	45.6	26.1	19.5	7.7	–	–	–	–
538 mulberries		80	85.0	36	151	1.3	8.1	0.0	8.1	0.0	–	–	–	0
539 mullet		100	75.2	115	481	19.8	0.0	0.0	0.0	4.0	44.0	36.0	20.0	34

per 100 g	fibre	non-starch polysaccharide	vit A	carotene	vit E	vit B$_1$	vit B$_2$	niacin	vit B$_6$	folate	vit C	sodium	calcium	iron	iodine
	g	g	µg	µg	mg	mg	mg	mg	mg	µg	mg	mg	mg	mg	µg
508 McDonalds strawberry sundae	0.4	0.0	60	133	0.4	0.04	0.17	0.1	0.04	5	1	56	111	0.1	–
509 McDonalds sweet and sour sauce	0.1	0.0	203	0	–	0.00	0.03	0.3	0.01	1	2	594	34	0.5	–
510 McDonalds vanilla frozen yogurt	–	0.0	48	–	–	0.05	0.23	0.5	–		0	100	140	0.3	–
511 medlars	9.2	–	–	–	–	–	–	–	–	–	2	6	30	0.5	–
512 melon seeds	–	–	0	0	-	0.17	0.15	11.8	–	58	0	99	71	7.6	–
513 melon, canteloupe	0.6	0.7	110	660	0.1	0.03	0.01	0.4	0.07	3	17	5	13	0.2	3
514 melon, galia	0.6	0.3	–	–	0.1	0.02	0.01	0.3	0.06	2	10	21	9	0.1	–
515 melon, honeydew	0.5	0.4	5	31	0.1	0.02	0.01	0.2	0.04	1	6	21	6	0.1	–
516 melon, watermelon	0.3	0.1	38	230	0.1	0.05	0.01	0.1	0.14	2	8	2	7	0.3	0
517 meringue (unfilled)	0.0	0.0	0	0	0.0	0.00	0.24	1.7	0.01	6	0	110	4	0.1	2
518 milk, calcium fortified	0.0	0.0	3	0	0.0	0.19	0.44	1.0	0.05	4	–	53	175	0.1	–
519 milk, Channel Island	0.0	0.0	58	71	0.1	0.04	0.19	1.0	0.06	6	1	54	130	0.1	–
520 milk, evaporated	0.0	0.0	122	100	0.2	0.07	0.42	2.2	0.07	11	1	180	290	0.3	11
521 milk, full cream	0.0	0.0	56	21	0.1	0.03	0.17	0.8	0.06	6	1	55	115	0.1	15
522 milk, goat	0.0	0.0	44	0	0.0	0.04	0.13	1.0	0.06	1	1	42	100	0.1	–
523 milk, semi-skimmed	0.0	0.0	23	9	0.0	0.04	0.18	0.9	0.06	6	1	55	120	0.1	15
524 milk, sheep	0.0	0.0	83	0	0.1	0.08	0.32	1.7	0.08	5	5	44	170	0.0	–
525 milk, skimmed	0.0	0.0	1	0	0.0	0.04	0.17	0.9	0.06	5	1	54	120	0.1	15
526 Milky Way	0.0	0.0	0	0	1.9	0.05	0.20	1.3	0.03	10	0	100	120	1.7	–
527 mincemeat (sweet)	3.0	1.3	2	9	–	0.04	0.02	0.5	0.10	8	0	140	30	1.5	–
528 mint	–	–	123	740	5.0	0.12	0.33	1.1	-	110	31	15	210	9.5	–
529 mint sauce	–	–	0	0	0.0	0.00	0.00	0.3	0.00	0	0	700	120	7.4	0
530 monkey nuts (peanuts, groundnuts)	7.3	6.2	0	0	10.1	1.14	0.10	19.3	0.59	110	0	2	60	2.5	20
531 monkfish	0.0	0.0	0	0	–	0.03	0.06	–	–	–	0	18	8	0.3	–
532 mooli (white radish)	1.5	–	0	0	0.0	0.03	0.02	0.6	0.07	38	24	27	30	0.4	–
533 muesli, no added sugar	11.1	7.7	0	0	3.2	0.30	0.30	7.5	–	–	0	29	49	3.4	–
534 muesli, Swiss style	8.1	6.1	0	0	3.2	0.50	0.70	8.8	1.60	140	0	380	120	5.6	–
535 muesli, with extra fruit	5.4	–	0	0	–	0.10	0.50	7.2	0.00	–	2	120	66	4.0	–
536 muffins	2.7	2.0	67	–	0.7	0.20	0.16	3.9	0.12	45	0	130	140	1.8	–
537 muffins, bran	8.5	7.7	81	–	0.9	0.21	0.16	7.6	0.25	31	0	770	120	3.3	–
538 mulberries	1.5	–	2	14	–	0.03	0.05	0.9	0.06	33	19	2	36	1.6	–
539 mullet	0.0	0.0	47	0	–	0.06	0.15	7.5	–	–	0	65	27	1.0	190

per 100 g		average serving	water	energy	energy	protein	carbohydrates	starch	sugars	fat	saturated	mono-unsaturated	poly-unsaturated	cholesterol
		g	g	kcal	kJ	g	g	g	g	g	%	%	%	mg
540 mushrooms, fried in butter		45	74.8	157	657	2.4	0.3	0.2	0.1	16.2	70.9	25.8	3.3	37
541 mushrooms, raw		45	92.6	13	54	1.8	0.4	0.2	0.2	0.5	–	–	–	0
542 mussels, boiled, weighed with shell		130	23.7	26	109	5.2	0.0	0.0	0.0	0.6	25.0	25.0	50.0	12
543 mustard and cress	¼ punnet	10	95.3	13	54	1.6	0.4	0.0	0.4	0.6	–	–	–	0
544 mustard leaves		95	94.6	17	71	2.0	1.9	1.4	0.5	0.2	–	–	–	0
545 naan	1	160	28.8	336	1406	8.9	50.1	44.6	5.5	12.5	–	–	–	6
546 nectarines		150	88.9	40	167	1.4	9.0	0.0	9.0	0.1	–	–	–	0
547 noodles, egg, boiled		230	84.3	62	260	2.2	13.0	12.8	0.2	0.5	25.0	50.0	25.0	6
548 noodles, egg, raw		30	9.1	391	1637	12.1	71.7	69.8	1.9	8.2	34.3	52.2	13.4	30
549 noodles, plain, boiled		230	82.2	62	260	2.4	13.0	12.8	0.2	0.4	–	–	–	–
550 noodles, plain, raw		30	10.6	388	1624	11.7	76.1	73.7	2.4	6.2	–	–	–	–
551 Nutri-Grain breakfast cereal		30	3.0	379	1586	9.8	68.3	59.9	8.4	9.3	–	–	–	–
552 oil, coconut		–	0.0	899	3763	0.0	0.0	0.0	0.0	99.9	91.1	7.1	1.8	0
553 oil, corn		–	0.0	899	3763	0.0	0.0	0.0	0.0	99.9	13.3	25.9	60.7	0
554 oil, cottonseed		–	0.0	899	3763	0.0	0.0	0.0	0.0	99.9	26.9	22.4	50.6	0
555 oil, mixed vegetable		–	0.0	899	3763	0.0	0.0	0.0	0.0	99.9	–	–	–	0
556 oil, olive		–	0.0	899	3763	0.0	0.0	0.0	0.0	99.9	14.8	73.4	11.8	0
557 oil, palm		–	0.0	899	3763	0.0	0.0	0.0	0.0	99.9	47.6	43.7	8.7	0
558 oil, peanut		–	0.0	899	3763	0.0	0.0	0.0	0.0	99.9	19.8	50.3	30.0	0
559 oil, rapeseed		–	0.0	899	3763	0.0	0.0	0.0	0.0	99.9	6.9	60.0	33.1	0
560 oil, safflower		–	0.0	899	3763	0.0	0.0	0.0	0.0	99.9	10.7	13.3	76.0	0
561 oil, sesame		–	0.1	881	3688	0.2	0.0	0.0	0.0	99.7	14.9	39.1	46.0	0
562 oil, soya		–	0.0	899	3763	0.0	0.0	0.0	0.0	99.9	15.4	24.6	60.0	0
563 oil, sunflower		–	0.0	899	3763	0.0	0.0	0.0	0.0	99.9	12.5	21.2	66.2	0
564 okra (ladies' fingers, bhindi)		50	87.9	28	117	2.5	2.7	0.5	2.3	0.9	42.9	14.3	42.9	0
565 olives in brine	8 olives	25	61.2	82	343	0.7	0.0	0.0	0.0	8.8	14.5	73.5	12.0	0
566 onion, fried		40	65.7	164	687	2.3	14.1	0.1	10.0	11.2	–	–	–	–
567 onion, raw	1 medium	160	89.0	36	151	1.2	7.9	0.0	5.6	0.2	–	–	–	0
568 orange juice, unsweetened	1 glass	200	89.2	36	151	0.5	8.8	0.0	8.8	0.1	–	–	–	0
569 oranges		160	60.3	26	109	0.8	5.9	0.0	5.9	0.1	–	–	–	0
570 oregano		5	81.8	66	276	2.2	9.7	–	–	2.0	–	–	–	0
571 ortaniques		95	86.0	49	205	1.0	11.7	0.0	11.7	0.2	–	–	–	0
572 Oxo cube		5	9.1	229	959	38.3	12.0	12.0	0.0	3.4	–	–	–	–

per 100 g	fibre	non-starch polysaccharide	vit A	carotene	vit E	vit B₁	vit B₂	niacin	vit B₆	folate	vit C	sodium	calcium	iron	iodine
	g	g	µg	µg	mg	mg	mg	mg	mg	µg	mg	mg	mg	mg	µg
540 mushrooms, fried in butter	3.0	1.5	174	85	0.4	0.09	0.34	2.7	0.19	11	1	150	11	1.0	11
541 mushrooms, raw	2.3	1.1	0	0	0.1	0.09	0.31	3.5	0.18	44	1	5	6	0.6	3
542 mussels, boiled, weighed with shell	0.0	0.0	–	0	–	0.00	0.08	1.7	0.01	–	0	63	59	2.3	23
543 mustard and cress	3.3	1.1	213	1280	0.7	0.04	0.04	1.3	0.15	60	33	19	50	1.0	–
544 mustard leaves	–	–	56	335	–	0.04	0.07	0.5	–	–	26	16	80	0.8	–
545 naan	2.2	1.9	96	60	1.4	0.19	0.10	3.0	0.13	14	0	380	160	1.3	19
546 nectarines	2.2	1.2	9	52	–	0.02	0.04	0.8	0.03	0	33	1	6	0.4	3
547 noodles, egg, boiled	1.0	0.6	2	0	–	0.01	0.01	0.7	0.01	1	0	15	5	0.3	–
548 noodles, egg, raw	5.0	2.9	37	0	–	0.26	0.10	4.7	0.10	29	0	180	28	1.5	–
549 noodles, plain, boiled	1.2	0.7	0	0	0.0	0.02	0.00	0.8	0.01	2	0	1	5	1.3	0
550 noodles, plain, raw	5.2	2.9	0	0	0.0	0.37	0.04	4.8	0.13	18	0	2	23	1.5	0
551 Nutri-Grain breakfast cereal	12.4	8.9	0	0	–	1.00	1.50	17.8	1.80	250	0	500	45	6.7	–
552 oil, coconut	0.0	0.0	0	0	0.7	0.00	0.00	0.0	0.00	0	0	0	0	0.0	–
553 oil, corn	0.0	0.0	0	0	17.2	0.00	0.00	0.0	0.00	0	0	0	0	0.0	–
554 oil, cottonseed	0.0	0.0	0	0	42.8	0.00	0.00	0.0	0.00	0	0	0	0	0.0	–
555 oil, mixed vegetable	0.0	0.0	0	0	–	0.00	0.00	0.0	0.00	0	0	0	0	0.0	–
556 oil, olive	0.0	0.0	–	–	5.1	0.00	0.00	0.0	0.00	0	0	0	0	0.4	–
557 oil, palm	0.0	0.0	0	0	33.1	0.00	0.00	0.0	0.00	0	0	0	0	0.0	–
558 oil, peanut	0.0	0.0	0	0	15.2	0.00	0.00	0.0	0.00	0	0	0	0	0.0	–
559 oil, rapeseed	0.0	0.0	0	0	22.2	0.00	0.00	0.0	0.00	0	0	0	0	0.0	–
560 oil, safflower	0.0	0.0	0	0	40.7	0.00	0.00	0.0	0.00	0	0	0	0	0.0	–
561 oil, sesame	0.0	0.0	0	0	–	0.01	0.07	0.1	0.00	0	0	2	10	0.1	–
562 oil, soya	0.0	0.0	0	0	16.3	0.00	0.00	0.0	0.00	0	0	0	0	0.0	–
563 oil, sunflower	0.0	0.0	0	0	49.2	0.00	0.00	0.0	0.00	0	0	0	0	0.0	–
564 okra (ladies' fingers, bhindi)	4.1	3.6	78	465	–	0.13	0.05	1.2	0.19	46	16	5	120	0.6	–
565 olives in brine	3.2	2.3	24	145	1.6	0.00	0.00	0.1	0.02	0	0	1800	49	0.8	–
566 onion, fried	3.2	3.1	7	40	1.9	0.08	0.01	0.5	0.10	38	3	4	47	0.8	6
567 onion, raw	1.5	1.4	2	10	0.3	0.13	0.00	1.0	0.20	17	5	3	25	0.3	3
568 orange juice, unsweetened	0.1	0.1	3	17	0.2	0.08	0.02	0.3	0.07	20	39	10	10	0.2	2
569 oranges	1.3	1.2	3	20	0.2	0.08	0.03	0.4	0.07	22	38	3	33	0.1	1
570 oregano	–	–	135	810	–	0.07	–	–	–	–	45	3	310	–	–
571 ortaniques	1.8	1.7	20	120	0.2	0.10	0.04	0.5	0.10	31	50	5	41	0.4	2
572 Oxo cube	0.0	0.0	0	0	–	–	–	–	–	–	0	10300	180	24.5	44

per 100 g		average serving	water	energy	energy	protein	carbohydrates	starch	sugars	fat	saturated	mono-unsaturated	poly-unsaturated	cholesterol
		g	g	kcal	kJ	g	g	g	g	g	%	%	%	mg
573 oxtail, stewed		–	20.5	92	385	11.6	0.0	0.0	0.0	5.1	–	–	–	–
574 oysters, weighed without shells	6 oysters	60	85.7	65	272	10.8	2.7	0.0	0.0	1.3	25.0	25.0	50.0	57
575 pakora (bhajia)	1	60	56.9	180	753	7.8	20.4	17.9	1.8	8.2	–	–	–	–
576 pancakes, sweet		110	43.4	301	1260	5.9	35.0	18.8	16.2	16.2	46.1	44.2	9.7	68
577 papadums, raw	1	10	12.1	272	1139	20.6	46.0	46.0	0.0	1.9	–	–	–	–
578 paratha	1	140	32.3	322	1348	8.0	43.2	42.1	1.1	14.3	–	–	–	–
579 parsley		5	83.1	34	142	3.0	2.7	0.4	2.3	1.3	–	–	–	0
580 parsnip, boiled		65	78.7	66	276	1.6	12.9	6.4	5.9	1.2	22.2	55.6	22.2	0
581 partridge, weighed with bone	½ bird	275	32.7	127	532	22.0	0.0	0.0	0.0	4.3	26.8	48.8	24.4	–
582 passion fruit (purple grenadilla)	25	45.7	22	92	1.7	3.5	0.0	3.5	0.2	33.3	33.3	33.3	0	
583 pastry, Danish	1 medium	110	21.6	374	1566	5.8	51.3	22.8	28.5	17.6	33.9	46.7	19.4	41
584 pastry, flaky, baked		–	7.7	560	2344	5.6	45.9	45.0	0.9	40.6	37.9	43.0	19.1	54
585 pastry, flaky, raw		–	30.1	424	1775	4.2	34.8	34.1	0.7	30.7	37.9	43.0	19.1	41
586 pastry, shortcrust, baked		–	7.2	521	2181	6.6	54.2	53.2	1.1	32.3	37.9	43.0	19.1	43
587 pastry, shortcrust, raw		–	20.0	449	1880	5.7	46.8	45.8	0.9	27.9	37.8	43.1	19.1	37
588 pastry, wholemeal, baked		–	7.4	499	2089	8.9	44.6	43.1	1.5	32.9	37.6	43.0	19.4	43
589 pastry, wholemeal, raw		–	20.0	431	1804	7.7	38.5	37.2	1.3	28.4	37.5	43.0	19.5	37
590 pawpaw	1 slice	140	66.4	27	113	0.4	6.6	0.0	6.6	0.1	–	–	–	0
591 peaches		120	80.0	30	126	0.9	6.8	0.0	6.8	0.1	–	–	–	0
592 peaches, canned in juice		120	86.7	39	163	0.6	9.7	0.0	9.7	0.0	–	–	–	0
593 peaches, canned in syrup		120	81.1	55	230	0.5	14.0	0.0	14.0	0.0	–	–	–	0
594 peanut butter		25	1.1	623	2608	22.6	13.1	6.4	6.7	53.7	22.8	41.4	35.8	0
595 peanuts (monkey nuts, ground nuts)	10 whole nuts	13	6.3	564	2361	25.6	12.5	6.3	6.2	46.1	18.8	48.4	32.8	0
596 peanuts and raisins		30	9.3	435	1821	15.3	37.5	3.5	34.0	26.0	18.9	48.4	32.8	0
597 peanuts, dry roasted		25	1.8	589	2466	25.5	10.3	6.5	3.8	49.8	18.9	48.3	32.8	0
598 peanuts, roasted and salted		25	1.9	602	2520	24.5	7.1	3.3	3.8	53.0	18.9	48.2	32.9	0
599 pear		150	76.3	36	151	0.3	9.1	0.0	9.1	0.1	–	–	–	0
600 pear, nashi (Asian pears)		150	77.5	26	109	0.3	6.3	0.0	6.3	0.1	–	–	–	0
601 peas, boiled		70	75.6	79	331	6.7	10.0	7.6	1.2	1.6	23.1	15.4	61.5	0
602 peas, frozen petit pois		70	81.1	49	205	5.0	5.5	0.0	3.0	0.9	25.0	12.5	62.5	0
603 peas, frozen, boiled		70	78.3	69	289	6.0	9.7	4.7	2.7	0.9	25.0	12.5	62.5	0
604 peas, pigeon, boiled		60	66.7	117	490	8.5	21.2	20.3	0.6	0.5	28.6	7.1	64.3	0
605 peas, sugar snap peas		70	88.4	33	138	3.1	4.7	1.3	3.4	0.3	–	–	–	0

per 100 g	fibre	non-starch polysaccharide	vit A	carotene	vit E	vit B₁	vit B₂	niacin	vit B₆	folate	vit C	sodium	calcium	iron	iodine
	g	g	µg	µg	mg	mg	mg	mg	mg	µg	mg	mg	mg	mg	µg
573 oxtail, stewed	0.0	0.0	0	0	0.2	0.01	0.11	3.8	0.05	3	0	72	5	1.4	–
574 oysters, weighed without shells	0.0	0.0	75	0	0.9	0.15	0.19	4.1	0.16	–	0	510	140	5.7	60
575 pakora (bhajia)	5.6	4.5	130	–	–	0.15	0.05	1.7	0.16	50	5	360	93	3.4	–
576 pancakes, sweet	0.9	0.8	58	12	0.3	0.10	0.17	1.9	0.09	8	1	53	110	0.8	24
577 papadums, raw	10.7	–	–	–	–	0.21	0.12	3.9	–	67	0	2850	81	13.0	–
578 paratha	4.4	4.0	140	–	0.7	0.18	0.04	4.1	0.14	16	0	120	84	2.0	–
579 parsley	8.2	5.0	673	4040	1.7	0.23	0.06	1.5	0.09	170	190	33	200	7.7	–
580 parsnip, boiled	4.4	4.7	5	30	1.0	0.07	0.01	1.1	0.09	48	10	4	50	0.6	–
581 partridge, weighed with bone	0.0	0.0	–	–	–	–	–	–	–	–	0	60	28	4.6	–
582 passion fruit (purple grenadilla)	–	2.0	77	460	–	0.02	0.07	1.1	–	–	14	12	7	0.8	–
583 pastry, Danish	2.7	1.6	–	–	0.0	0.13	0.07	2.1	0.07	20	0	190	92	1.3	–
584 pastry, flaky, baked	2.1	1.8	198	165	2.0	0.14	0.02	2.1	0.07	7	0	460	84	1.3	13
585 pastry, flaky, raw	1.6	1.4	146	125	1.5	0.14	0.01	1.7	0.07	10	1	350	64	1.0	10
586 pastry, shortcrust, baked	2.5	2.2	157	130	1.6	0.16	0.02	2.4	0.08	8	0	480	99	1.5	13
587 pastry, shortcrust, raw	2.2	1.9	134	115	1.4	0.19	0.02	2.1	0.09	13	0	410	85	1.3	11
588 pastry, wholemeal, baked	6.0	6.3	157	130	2.4	0.25	0.05	5.5	0.26	20	0	410	28	2.8	–
589 pastry, wholemeal, raw	5.2	5.4	134	115	2.1	0.28	0.05	4.9	0.30	34	0	360	24	2.4	–
590 pawpaw	1.7	1.7	98	585	–	0.02	0.03	0.3	0.02	1	45	4	17	0.4	–
591 peaches	2.1	1.3	9	53	–	0.02	0.04	0.7	0.02	3	28	1	6	0.4	3
592 peaches, canned in juice	0.9	0.8	11	67	0	0.01	0.01	0.7	0.02	2	6	12	4	0.4	–
593 peaches, canned in syrup	0.9	0.9	13	75	–	0.01	0.01	0.7	0.02	7	5	4	3	0.2	–
594 peanut butter	6.8	5.4	0	0	5.0	0.17	0.09	17.4	0.58	53	0	350	37	2.1	–
595 peanuts (monkey nuts, ground nuts)	7.3	6.2	0	0	10.1	1.14	0.10	19.3	0.59	110	0	2	60	2.5	20
596 peanuts and raisins	6.8	4.4	1	5	5.7	0.69	0.08	11.1	0.44	65	0	27	53	2.1	11
597 peanuts, dry roasted	7.4	6.4	0	0	1.1	0.18	0.13	18.6	0.54	66	0	790	52	2.1	19
598 peanuts, roasted and salted	6.9	6.0	0	0	0.7	0.18	0.10	18.9	0.63	52	0	400	37	1.3	19
599 pear	–	2.0	3	16	0.5	0.02	0.03	0.2	0.02	2	5	3	10	0.2	1
600 pear, nashi (Asian pears)	–	1.3	0	0	0.5	0.03	0.03	0.3	0.04	3	4	5	4	0.1	1
601 peas, boiled	4.7	4.5	42	250	0.2	0.70	0.03	2.9	0.09	27	16	0	19	1.5	2
602 peas, frozen petit pois	6.4	4.5	68	405	0.2	0.13	0.12	2.4	0.09	50	8	2	42	1.6	2
603 peas, frozen, boiled	7.3	5.1	68	405	0.2	0.26	0.09	2.5	0.09	47	12	2	35	1.6	2
604 peas, pigeon, boiled	6.2	–	2	11	–	0.15	0.04	1.4	–	25	0	14	52	1.3	–
605 peas, sugar snap peas	–	1.3	30	180	–	0.11	0.11	1.0	0.11	4	18	62	41	0.6	–

per 100 g		average serving	water	energy	energy	protein	carbohydrates	starch	sugars	fat	saturated	mono-unsaturated	poly-unsaturated	cholesterol
		g	g	kcal	kJ	g	g	g	g	g	%	%	%	mg
606 pecan nuts (hickory nuts)	3 nuts	18	3.7	689	2884	9.2	5.8	1.5	4.3	70.1	8.5	63.5	28.0	0
607 peppers, green	1/2 pepper	80	93.3	15	63	0.8	2.6	0.1	2.4	0.3	33.3	0.0	66.7	0
608 peppers, red		80	90.4	32	134	1.0	6.4	0.1	6.1	0.4	33.3	0.0	66.7	0
609 persimmon (kaki, sharon fruit)	110	79.9	73	306	0.8	18.6	0.0	18.6	0.0	–	–	–	0	
610 pheasant, weighed with bone	1/2 bird	200	35.8	134	561	20.3	0.0	0.0	0.0	5.9	35.7	51.8	12.5	–
611 physalis (Cape gooseberry, Chinese lantern)	5	10	82.9	53	222	1.8	11.1	0.0	11.1	0.2	–	–	–	0
612 pigeon, weighed with bone		240	25.2	101	423	12.2	0.0	0.0	0.0	5.8	–	–	–	–
613 pignolias (pine nuts, pine kernels)		12	2.7	688	2880	14.0	4.0	0.1	3.9	68.6	7.0	30.3	62.7	0
614 pilchards, canned in tomato	small tin	215	70.0	126	527	18.8	0.7	0.1	0.6	5.4	22.4	30.6	46.9	56
615 pine nuts (pignolias, pine kernels)		12	2.7	688	2880	14.0	4.0	0.1	3.9	68.6	7.0	30.3	62.7	0
616 pineapple	1 slice	80	86.5	41	172	0.4	10.1	0.0	10.1	0.2	–	–	–	0
617 pineapple guava (feijoa)		–	85.0	47	197	0.9	10.3	0.3	10.0	0.5	–	–	–	0
618 pineapple juice, unsweetened	1 glass	200	87.8	41	172	0.3	10.5	0.0	10.5	0.1	–	–	–	0
619 pineapple, canned in juice	2 rings/12 chunks	80	86.8	47	197	0.3	12.2	0.0	12.2	0.0	–	–	–	0
620 pineapple, canned in syrup	2 rings/12 chunks	80	82.2	64	268	0.5	16.5	0.0	16.5	0.0	–	–	–	0
621 pistacchio nuts, roasted and salted	10 nuts	10	2.1	601	2516	17.9	8.2	2.5	5.7	55.4	14.0	52.2	33.8	0
622 pizza, average takeaway	7 inch deep pan	250	–	242	1015	15.4	25.8	–	–	8.6	35.4	44.9	19.7	21
623 pizza, beef and onion	7 inch deep pan	290	–	258	1078	15.3	27.8	–	–	9.4	–	–	–	–
624 pizza, beef, chicken and onion	7 inch deep pan	290	–	257	1074	19.5	25.5	–	–	8.4	–	–	–	–
625 pizza, cheese	7 inch deep pan	220	–	223	932	12.2	32.5	–	–	5.1	51.0	32.7	16.3	15
626 pizza, chicken and pineapple, Hawaiian)	7 inch deep pan	290	–	284	1191	14.9	22.3	–	–	15.0	–	–	–	–
627 pizza, chicken curry and peas	7 inch deep pan	290	–	288	1207	13.2	33.3	–	–	11.4	–	–	–	–
628 pizza, chicken, mushroom and tomato	7 inch deep pan	290	–	214	898	17.3	25.8	–	–	4.6	–	–	–	–
629 pizza, combination supreme	7 inch deep pan	360	–	178	747	14.6	25.1	–	–	2.2	41.5	45.8	12.7	20
630 pizza, curry beef and peas	7 inch deep pan	290	–	249	1044	15.9	25.8	–	–	9.1	24.6	46.5	29.0	29
631 pizza, onion, tomato, green pepper, mushroom	7 inch deep pan	300	–	160	672	12.3	23.3	–	–	2.0	–	–	–	–
632 pizza, pepperoni, beef, salami and mushroom	7 inch deep pan	290	–	294	1232	17.9	16.1	–	–	17.5	–	–	–	–
633 pizza, shrimp and cucumber	7 inch deep pan	290	–	242	1015	15.7	24.1	–	–	9.2	–	–	–	–

per 100 g	fibre	non-starch polysaccharide	vit A	carotene	vit E	vit B$_1$	vit B$_2$	niacin	vit B$_6$	folate	vit C	sodium	calcium	iron	iodine
	g	g	µg	µg	mg	mg	mg	mg	mg	µg	mg	mg	mg	mg	µg
606 pecan nuts (hickory nuts)	–	4.7	8	50	4.3	0.71	0.15	5.5	0.19	39	0	1	61	2.2	–
607 peppers, green	1.9	1.6	44	265	0.8	0.01	0.01	0.2	0.30	36	120	4	8	0.4	1
608 peppers, red	1.9	1.6	640	3840	0.8	0.01	0.03	1.5	0.36	21	140	4	8	0.3	1
609 persimmon (kaki, sharon fruit)	–	1.6	158	950	–	0.03	0.05	0.3	–	7	19	5	10	0.1	–
610 pheasant, weighed with bone	0.0	0.0	–	–	–	0.01	0.13	7.9	0.26	9	0	66	31	5.3	–
611 physalis (Cape gooseberry, Chinese lantern)	–	–	238	1430	–	0.05	0.02	0.6	–	–	49	1	10	2.0	–
612 pigeon, weighed with bone	0.0	0.0	–	–	0.0	0.12	–	5.4	0.36	3	0	46	7	8.5	–
613 pignolias (pine nuts, pine kernels)	–	1.9	2	10	13.7	0.73	0.19	6.9	–	–	0	1	11	5.6	–
614 pilchards, canned in tomato	0.0	0.0	32	142	0.7	0.02	0.29	11.1	0.27	–	0	370	300	2.7	64
615 pine nuts (pignolias, pine kernels)	–	1.9	2	10	13.7	0.73	0.19	6.9	–	–	0	1	11	5.6	–
616 pineapple	1.3	1.2	3	18	0.1	0.08	0.03	0.4	0.09	5	12	2	18	0.2	0
617 pineapple guava (feijoa)	–	–	5	31	0.2	0.00	0.01	0.2	0.05	–	29	3	5	0.1	–
618 pineapple juice, unsweetened	0.0	0.0	1	8	0.0	0.06	0.01	0.2	0.05	8	11	8	8	0.2	0
619 pineapple, canned in juice	0.8	0.5	2	12	0.1	0.09	0.01	0.3	0.09	1	11	1	8	0.5	0
620 pineapple, canned in syrup	0.8	0.7	2	11	0.1	0.07	0.01	0.3	0.07	1	13	2	6	0.2	0
621 pistacchio nuts, roasted and salted	–	6.1	22	130	4.2	0.70	0.23	5.6	–	58	0	530	110	3.0	–
622 pizza, average takeaway	0.7	0.0	96	131	1.8	0.09	0.10	6.1	0.12	50	2	635	136	1.0	–
623 pizza, beef and onion	0.4	0.0	102	120	–	0.04	0.06	3.1	–	–	1	466	75	0.6	–
624 pizza, beef, chicken and onion	0.1	0.0	98	96	–	0.09	0.08	4.4	–	–	4	943	258	2.5	–
625 pizza, cheese	2.0	0.0	206	532	1.4	0.29	0.26	3.9	0.07	93	2	532	185	0.9	–
626 pizza, chicken and pineapple , Hawaian)	0.2	0.0	105	96	–	0.09	0.09	7.5	–	–	3	943	304	1.4	–
627 pizza, chicken curry and peas	0.7	0.0	111	36	–	0.07	0.09	6.1	–	–	1	516	68	0.6	–
628 pizza, chicken, mushroom and tomato	0.3	0.0	96	96	–	0.03	0.04	2.7	–	–	1	590	85	0.7	–
629 pizza, combination supreme	0.6	0.0	48	84	1.2	0.06	0.06	6.4	0.13	24	2	583	94	0.8	–
630 pizza, curry beef and peas	0.6	0.0	129	168	2.8	0.07	0.08	12.6	0.20	9	3	459	84	0.6	–
631 pizza, onion, tomato, green pepper, mushroom	0.8	0.0	52	120	–	0.05	0.08	5.8	–	–	2	481	87	0.8	–
632 pizza, pepperoni, beef, salami and mushroom	0.3	0.0	90	84	–	0.07	0.01	10.8	–	–	1	1297	270	0.8-	–
633 pizza, shrimp and cucumber	0.5	0.0	54	72	–	0.03	0.04	8.2	–	–	1	505	87	0.7	–

per 100 g		average serving	water	energy	energy	protein	carbohydrates	starch	sugars	fat	saturated	mono-unsaturated	poly-unsaturated	cholesterol
		g	g	kcal	kJ	g	g	g	g	g	%	%	%	mg
634 pizza, shrimp, squid and mushroom	7 inch deep pan	290	–	248	1040	17.5	26.3	–	–	8.1	–	–	–	–
635 plaice		130	79.5	79	331	16.7	0.0	0.0	0.0	1.4	22.2	44.4	33.3	42
636 plaice goujons, fried		100	27.9	426	1783	8.5	27.0	26.1	0.9	32.3	–	–	–	–
637 plaice, battered, fried		200	52.4	279	1168	15.8	14.4	14.1	0.3	18.0	8.8	52.4	38.8	–
638 plaintain, boiled		200	68.5	112	469	0.8	28.5	23.0	5.5	0.2	–	–	–	0
639 plums	1	55	78.9	34	142	0.5	8.3	0.0	8.3	0.1	–	–	–	0
640 plums, Victoria	1	55	80.8	37	155	0.5	9.0	0.0	9.0	0.1	–	–	–	0
641 plums, yellow	1	55	85.4	24	100	0.5	5.7	0.0	5.7	0.1	–	–	–	0
642 pomegranate		50	52.0	33	138	0.9	7.7	0.0	7.7	0.1	–	–	–	0
643 pomelo (shaddock)	half	125	55.0	18	75	0.4	4.1	0.0	4.1	0.1	–	–	–	0
644 pork pie	individual	140	36.8	376	1574	9.8	24.9	24.4	0.5	27.0	40.2	49.2	10.6	52
645 pork, belly, grilled		170	43.0	398	1666	21.1	0.0	0.0	0.0	34.8	40.1	43.8	16.1	105
646 pork, leg, roast		150	61.6	185	774	30.7	0.0	0.0	0.0	6.9	39.3	44.3	16.4	110
647 pork, loin chops, grilled		150	33.1	133	557	19.1	0.0	0.0	0.0	6.3	40.0	43.6	16.4	65
648 pork, trotters and tail, salted		–	53.5	280	1172	19.8	0.0	0.0	0.0	22.3	–	–	–	–
649 porridge (oatmeal), made with milk		110	74.8	116	486	4.8	13.7	9.0	4.7	5.1	57.4	31.9	10.6	14
650 porridge (oatmeal), made with water		110	87.4	49	205	1.5	9.0	9.0	0.0	1.1	20.0	40.0	40.0	0
651 port		50	71.1	157	657	0.1	12.0	0.0	12.0	0.0	–	–	–	0
652 potato crisps		30	1.9	546	2286	5.6	49.3	48.6	0.7	37.6	29.6	38.6	31.8	0
653 potato crisps, low fat		30	1.1	483	2022	6.6	63.0	62.0	1.0	21.5	29.8	38.5	31.7	0
654 potato hoops		30	2.8	523	2189	3.9	58.5	58.0	0.5	32.0	–	–	–	0
655 potatoes, chips		165	56.5	189	791	3.9	30.1	29.5	0.6	6.7	9.5	52.4	38.1	0
656 potatoes, croquettes, fried	3 croquettes	240	58.2	214	896	3.7	21.6	21.1	0.5	13.1	13.6	25.6	60.8	0
657 potatoes, French fries		120	43.8	280	1172	3.3	34.0	32.7	1.3	15.5	39.2	46.6	14.2	–
658 potatoes, frozen oven chips		165	58.5	162	678	3.2	29.8	29.1	0.7	4.2	45.0	40.0	15.0	0
659 potatoes, microwave chips		165	50.4	221	925	3.6	32.1	31.5	0.6	9.6	–	–	–	
660 potatoes, new, boiled		175	81.1	66	276	1.4	15.4	14.4	1.0	0.3	–	–	–	0
661 potatoes, old, baked		180	62.6	136	569	3.9	31.7	30.5	1.2	0.2	–	–	–	0
662 potatoes, old, boiled		175	80.3	72	301	1.8	17.0	16.3	0.7	0.1	–	–	–	0
663 potatoes, roast		200	64.7	149	624	2.9	25.9	25.3	0.6	4.5	–	–	–	0
664 prawns, boiled, weighed with shells		150	26.6	41	172	8.6	0.0	0.0	0.0	0.7	40.0	40.0	20.0	31

per 100 g	fibre	non-starch polysaccharide	vit A	carotene	vit E	vit B₁	vit B₂	niacin	vit B₆	folate	vit C	sodium	calcium	iron	iodine
	g	g	µg	µg	mg	mg	mg	mg	mg	µg	mg	mg	mg	mg	µg
634 pizza, shrimp, squid and mushroom	0.5	0.0	58	72	–	0.03	0.05	3.3	–	–	1	565	79	0.6	–
635 plaice	0.0	0.0	0	0	–	0.20	0.19	6.3	0.22	11	0	120	45	0.3	33
636 plaice goujons, fried	1.4	–	10	3	6.8	0.08	0.10	2.9	0.16	6	0	470	120	1.2	–
637 plaice, battered, fried	0.5	–	0	0	–	0.20	0.15	4.9	–	–	0	220	93	1.0	31
638 plaintain, boiled	2.2	1.2	58	350	0.2	0.03	0.04	0.6	0.24	22	9	4	5	0.5	–
639 plums	2.2	1.5	46	275	0.6	0.05	0.03	1.1	0.05	3	4	2	12	0.4	0
640 plums, Victoria	1.8	1.7	46	275	0.6	0.05	0.03	0.6	0.05	3	6	2	10	0.4	0
641 plums, yellow	–	1.0	20	120	0.6	0.03	0.05	0.7	0.05	3	5	1	7	0.2	0
642 pomegranate	–	2.2	4	21	–	0.03	0.03	0.3	0.20	–	8	1	8	0.5	–
643 pomelo (shaddock)	0.5	–	2	14	0.1	0.03	0.02	0.2	0.02	16	27	1	16	0.2	–
644 pork pie	0.9	0.9	0	0	0.4	0.16	0.09	3.9	0.06	3	0	720	47	1.4	7
645 pork, belly, grilled	0.0	0.0	0	0	0.1	0.53	0.11	8.1	0.23	4	0	95	11	1.0	3
646 pork, leg, roast	0.0	0.0	0	0	0.0	0.85	0.35	12.3	0.41	7	0	79	9	1.3	3
647 pork, loin chops, grilled	0.0	0.0	0	0	0.0	0.52	0.15	8.1	0.24	4	0	50	5	0.7	2
648 pork, trotters and tail, salted	0.0	0.0	0	0	–	0.06	0.20	4.6	–	3	0	1615	129	0.7	–
649 porridge (oatmeal), made with milk	0.8	0.8	57	21	0.3	0.10	0.17	1.3	0.06	7	1	620	120	0.6	–
650 porridge (oatmeal), made with water	0.8	0.8	0	0	0.2	0.06	0.01	0.4	0.01	4	0	560	7	0.5	–
651 port	0.0	0.0	0	0	0.0	0.00	0.01	0.1	0.01	0	0	4	4	0.4	–
652 potato crisps	10.7	4.9	0	2	3.1	0.11	0.07	5.9	0.32	41	27	1070	37	1.8	–
653 potato crisps, low fat	13.7	6.3	0	2	1.8	0.19	0.14	6.6	0.53	41	14	1070	36	1.8	–
654 potato hoops	–	2.6	0	0	–	–	–	–	–	–	3	1070	22	1.0	–
655 potatoes, chips	3.0	2.2	0	0	–	0.24	0.02	1.6	0.32	43	9	12	11	0.8	5
656 potatoes, croquettes, fried	–	1.3	–	–	–	0.08	0.08	2.4	0.22	2	2	420	44	0.9	–
657 potatoes, French fries	3.1	2.1	0	0	1.0	0.08	0.05	3.1	0.36	–	4	310	14	1.0	–
658 potatoes, frozen oven chips	2.8	2.0	0	0	0.4	0.11	0.04	3.0	0.37	21	12	53	12	0.8	–
659 potatoes, microwave chips	3.1	2.9	0	0	–	0.12	0.07	3.0	0.29	20	11	40	17	1.0	6
660 potatoes, new, boiled	1.6	1.5	0	0	0.1	0.09	0.06	0.7	0.36	10	15	10	13	1.6	3
661 potatoes, old, baked	–	2.7	0	0	0.1	0.37	0.02	2.0	0.54	44	14	12	11	0.7	5
662 potatoes, old, boiled	1.4	1.2	0	0	0.1	0.18	0.01	0.9	0.33	26	6	7	5	0.4	3
663 potatoes, roast	2.4	1.8	0	0	–	0.23	0.02	1.4	0.31	36	8	9	8	0.7	4
664 prawns, boiled, weighed with shells	0.0	0.0	0	0	–	0.01	0.06	1.8	0.03	–	0	610	55	0.4	11

per 100 g		average serving	water	energy	energy	protein	carbohydrates	starch	sugars	fat	saturated	mono-unsaturated	poly-unsaturated	cholesterol
		g	g	kcal	kJ	g	g	g	g	g	%	%	%	mg
665 prickly pear (cactus fruit)		75	85.2	49	205	0.7	11.5	0.0	11.5	0.3	–	–	–	0
666 prunes, stewed without sugar	6 prunes	25	60.4	81	339	1.4	19.5	0.0	19.5	0.3	–	–	–	0
667 Puffed Wheat breakfast cereal	20	2.5	321	1344	14.2	67.3	67.0	0.3	1.3	20.0	20.0	60.0	0	
668 pumpkin seeds		15	5.6	569	2382	24.4	15.2	14.1	1.1	45.6	19.2	30.7	50.1	0
669 pumpkin, boiled		65	94.9	13	54	0.6	2.1	0.1	1.8	0.3	–	–	–	0
670 Queensland nuts (macadamia nuts)	6 nuts	10	1.3	748	3131	7.9	4.8	0.8	4.0	77.6	15.2	82.6	2.2	0
671 quiche	slice	90	46.7	314	1314	12.5	17.3	15.7	1.6	22.2	50.2	38.5	11.2	140
672 quince		150	84.2	26	109	0.3	6.3	0.0	6.3	0.1	–	–	–	0
673 quinoa		–	11.5	309	1293	13.8	55.7	47.6	6.1	5.0	12.5	35.0	52.5	0
674 rabbit, weighed with bone	1/4 rabbit	210	32.5	91	381	13.9	0.0	0.0	0.0	3.9	43.2	21.6	35.1	69
675 raddiccio		20	92.9	14	59	1.4	1.7	0.0	1.7	0.2	–	–	–	0
676 radish	4 radishes	30	95.4	12	50	0.7	1.9	0.0	1.9	0.2	–	–	–	0
677 radish, white (mooli)		30	93.0	15	63	0.8	2.9	0.0	2.9	0.1	–	–	–	0
678 raisins	1 tablespoon	30	13.2	272	1139	2.1	69.3	0.0	69.3	0.4	–	–	–	–
679 rambutan (hairy lychee)	4 fruits	95	80.4	69	289	1.0	16.3	0.0	16.3	0.4	–	–	–	0
680 raspberries		80	87.0	25	105	1.4	4.6	0.0	4.6	0.3	–	–	–	0
681 Ready Brek breakfast cereal		30	6.3	389	1628	12.4	69.5	67.7	1.7	8.7	18.2	43.9	37.9	0
682 redcurrants		80	82.8	21	88	1.1	4.4	0.0	4.4	0.0	–	–	–	0
683 rhubarb		140	94.2	7	29	0.9	0.8	0.0	0.8	0.1	–	–	–	0
684 Rice Krispies breakfast cereal		20	3.8	369	1545	6.1	89.7	79.1	10.6	0.9	37.5	25.0	37.5	0
685 rice pudding, canned		200	77.6	89	373	3.4	14.0	5.8	8.2	2.5	66.7	29.2	4.2	9
686 rice, brown, boiled		180	66.0	141	590	2.6	32.1	31.6	0.5	1.1	30.0	30.0	40.0	0
687 rice, brown, raw		40	13.9	357	1494	6.7	81.3	80.0	1.3	2.8	29.2	29.2	41.7	0
688 rice, white, boiled		180	68.0	138	578	2.6	30.9	30.9	0.0	1.3	27.3	27.3	45.5	0
689 rice, white, raw		30	11.4	383	1603	7.3	85.8	85.8	0.0	3.6	29.0	29.0	41.9	0
690 Ricicles breakfast cereal		20	3.0	383	1603	4.3	96.3	56.5	39.8	0.5	40.0	20.0	40.0	0
691 rock salmon (dogfish)		150	68.3	154	645	16.6	0.0	0.0	0.0	9.7	20.9	38.8	40.3	76
692 rock salmon (dogfish), battered, fried		200	49.9	244	1021	15.4	7.1	7.0	0.1	17.3	–	–	–	0
693 roe, cod (hard)		120	73.7	104	435	21.7	0.0	0.0	0.0	1.9	28.6	28.6	42.9	330
694 roe, herring (soft)		85	80.0	91	381	16.8	0.0	0.0	0.0	2.6	27.8	33.3	38.9	575
695 sago		–	12.6	355	1486	0.2	94.0	94.0	0.0	0.2	–	–	–	0
696 sago pudding, skimmed milk		200	76.0	93	389	4.0	20.1	9.3	10.9	0.2	–	–	–	2

per 100 g	fibre	non-starch polysaccharide	vit A	carotene	vit E	vit B₁	vit B₂	niacin	vit B₆	folate	vit C	sodium	calcium	iron	iodine
	g	g	µg	µg	mg	mg	mg	mg	mg	µg	mg	mg	mg	mg	µg
665 prickly pear (cactus fruit)	–	–	8	45	–	0.02	0.04	0.4	–	–	22	4	53	0.4	–
666 prunes, stewed without sugar	7.4	3.3	13	78	–	0.04	0.08	0.9	0.10	0	0	6	19	1.5	–
667 Puffed Wheat breakfast cereal	8.8	5.6	0	0	2.0	0.00	0.06	8.1	0.14	19	0	4	26	4.6	–
668 pumpkin seeds	–	5.3	38	230	–	0.23	0.32	8.8	–	–	0	18	39	10.0	–
669 pumpkin, boiled	0.5	1.1	159	955	1.1	0.14	0.00	0.2	0.03	10	7	76	23	0.1	–
670 Queensland nuts (macadamia nuts)	–	5.3	0	0	1.5	0.28	0.06	3.3	0.28	–	0	–	47	1.6	–
671 quiche	0.7	0.6	202	100	0.9	0.08	0.23	3.5	0.08	13	0	340	260	1.0	31
672 quince	5.8	–	0	0	–	0.02	0.02	0.2	0.04	–	15	3	14	0.3	–
673 quinoa	–	–	–	–	–	0.20	0.40	4.8	0.00	–	0	61	79	7.8	–
674 rabbit, weighed with bone	0.0	0.0	–	–	–	0.04	0.14	6.9	0.26	2	0	16	6	1.0	–
675 raddiccio	–	1.8	0	0	–	0.09	0.15	0.5	0.08	15	5	7	22	0.3	–
676 radish	0.9	0.9	0	0	0.0	0.03	0.00	0.5	0.07	38	17	11	19	0.6	1
677 radish, white (mooli)	1.5	–	0	0	0.0	0.03	0.02	0.6	0.07	38	24	27	30	0.4	–
678 raisins	6.1	2.0	2	12	–	0.12	0.05	0.8	0.25	10	1	60	46	3.8	–
679 rambutan (hairy lychee)	1.3	–	0	0	–	0.02	0.06	0.7	–	–	78	1	14	0.1	–
680 raspberries	6.7	2.5	1	6	0.5	0.03	0.05	0.8	0.06	33	32	3	25	0.7	–
681 Ready Brek breakfast cereal	6.8	7.2	0	0	1.2	1.50	0.09	12.2	1.50	53	0	23	65	4.8	–
682 redcurrants	7.4	3.4	4	25	0.1	0.04	0.06	0.3	0.05	–	40	2	36	1.2	–
683 rhubarb	2.3	1.4	10	60	0.2	0.03	0.03	0.4	0.02	7	6	3	93	0.3	–
684 Rice Krispies breakfast cereal	1.1	0.5	0	0	0.6	1.00	1.50	17.4	1.80	250	0	1260	20	6.7	–
685 rice pudding, canned	–	0.2	–	–	–	0.03	0.14	0.9	0.02	–	0	50	93	0.2	–
686 rice, brown, boiled	1.5	0.8	0	0	0.3	0.14	0.02	1.9	–	10	0	1	4	0.5	–
687 rice, brown, raw	3.8	1.9	0	0	0.8	0.59	0.07	6.8	–	49	0	3	10	1.4	–
688 rice, white, boiled	1.0	0.1	0	0	0.0	0.01	0.00	1.5	0.07	4	0	1	18	0.2	5
689 rice, white, raw	2.7	0.4	0	0	0.1	0.41	0.02	5.8	0.31	20	0	4	51	0.5	14
690 Ricicles breakfast cereal	0.9	0.3	0	0	–	1.00	1.50	17.0	1.80	250	0	880	20	6.7	–
691 rock salmon (dogfish)	0.0	0.0	190	0	–	0.17	0.29	6.0	0.37	3	0	120	8	0.9	–
692 rock salmon (dogfish), battered, fried	0.3	0.3	86	0	1.9	0.06	0.09	–	–	–	0	270	39	1.0-	–
693 roe, cod (hard)	0.0	0.0	79	0	6.2	0.78	0.49	5.1	0.32	–	0	110	11	1.0	–
694 roe, herring (soft)	0.0	0.0	–	0	2.8	0.00	0.29	4.4	–	–	0	120	5	0.5	–
695 sago		0.5	0	0	0.0	0.00	0.00	0.0	0.00	0	0	3	10	1.2	–
696 sago pudding, skimmed milk	0.2	0.1	1	0	0.0	0.04	0.17	1.0	0.06	3	1	59	130	0.1	–

per 100 g		average serving g	water g	energy kcal	energy kJ	protein g	carbohydrates g	starch g	sugars g	fat g	saturated %	mono-unsaturated %	poly-unsaturated %	cholesterol mg
697 sago pudding, whole milk		200	72.4	129	540	3.9	19.9	9.3	10.7	4.3	65.9	29.3	4.9	1
698 saithe (coley)		100	80.2	82	343	18.3	0.0	0.0	0.0	1.0	14.3	42.9	42.9	40
699 salad cream		20	47.2	348	1457	1.5	16.7	0.0	16.7	31.0	13.2	21.0	65.8	43
700 salad cream, reduced calorie		20	–	194	812	1.0	9.4	0.0	9.2	17.2	15.3	28.8	55.8	7
701 salami	4 slices	20	28.0	491	2055	19.3	1.9	1.9	0.0	45.2	–	–	–	79
702 salmon		100	67.2	180	753	20.2	0.0	0.0	0.0	11.0	20.2	46.8	33.0	50
703 salmon, canned		100	71.3	153	640	23.5	0.0	0.0	0.0	6.6	23.2	42.9	33.9	28
704 salmon, smoked		25	64.9	142	594	25.4	0.0	0.0	0.0	4.5	20.5	46.2	33.3	35
705 salsify (scozonera)		50	83.3	27	113	1.3	10.2	3.5	1.5	0.3	–	–	–	–
706 samosa, meat		70	20.4	593	2482	5.1	17.9	16.8	1.0	56.1	–	–	–	–
707 samosa, vegetable		70	31.5	472	1976	3.1	22.3	20.1	1.9	41.8	–	–	–	–
708 sapodilla		–	76.3	69	289	0.6	15.5	0.8	14.7	0.9	–	–	–	0
709 sardines, canned in oil	4 fish	100	58.4	217	908	23.7	0.0	0.0	0.0	13.6	22.8	38.2	39.0	65
710 sardines, canned in tomato	4 fish	100	65.0	177	741	17.8	0.5	0.0	0.5	11.6	31.7	32.7	35.6	76
711 sardines, fresh	6 fish	80	67.7	165	691	20.6	0.0	0.0	0.0	9.2	34.2	31.6	34.2	–
712 satsumas		95	62.1	26	109	0.6	6.0	0.0	6.0	0.1	–	–	–	0
713 sausage roll, flaky pastry	medium	60	23.6	477	1997	7.1	32.3	31.1	1.2	36.4	39.1	45.5	15.5	49
714 sausage roll, short pastry	medium	60	22.3	459	1921	8.0	37.5	36.2	1.3	31.9	39.3	45.7	15.0	43
715 sausages, beef	1 large sausage	40	50.3	299	1252	9.6	11.7	9.9	1.8	24.1	44.2	49.6	6.2	40
716 sausages, beef, grilled	1 large sausage	40	47.9	265	1109	13.0	15.2	12.8	2.4	17.3	41.4	50.6	8.0	42
717 sausages, frankfurters		50	59.5	274	1147	9.5	3.0	3.0	0.0	25.0	–	–	–	46
718 sausages, low fat	1 large sausage	40	61.9	166	695	12.5	8.1	7.6	0.5	9.5	37.8	45.6	16.7	44
719 sausages, low fat, grilled	1 large sausage	40	50.1	229	959	16.2	10.8	9.9	0.9	13.8	37.9	45.5	16.7	55
720 sausages, pork	1 large sausage	40	45.4	367	1536	10.6	9.5	8.1	1.4	32.1	40.1	48.7	11.2	47
721 sausages, pork, grilled	1 large sausage	40	45.1	318	1331	13.3	11.5	9.7	1.8	24.6	40.9	47.4	11.6	53
722 sausages, saveloys	1 sausage	65	56.7	262	1097	9.9	10.1	10.1	0.0	20.5	–	–	–	45
723 scampi, in crumb, fried		170	39.4	316	1323	12.2	28.9	28.9	0.0	17.6	10.8	38.0	51.3	110
724 scones, cheese		50	26.9	363	1520	10.1	43.2	40.9	2.3	17.8	–	–	–	–
725 scones, fruit		50	25.3	316	1323	7.3	52.9	36.0	16.9	9.8	35.1	39.4	25.5	27
726 scones, plain		50	22.9	362	1515	7.2	53.8	47.9	5.9	14.6	35.0	39.3	25.7	29
727 scones, wholemeal	1	50	26.9	326	1365	8.7	43.1	37.1	5.9	14.4	34.8	39.1	26.1	27
728 scones, wholemeal, fruit		50	24.1	324	1356	8.1	47.2	33.0	14.2	12.8	–	–	–	–
729 scones, wholemeal, plain		50	26.9	326	1365	8.7	43.1	37.1	5.9	14.4	34.8	39.1	26.1	27

per 100 g	fibre	non-starch polysaccharide	vit A	carotene	vit E	vit B$_1$	vit B$_2$	niacin	vit B$_6$	folate	vit C	sodium	calcium	iron	iodine
	g	g	µg	µg	mg	mg	mg	mg	mg	µg	mg	mg	mg	mg	µg
697 sago pudding, whole milk	0.2	0.1	60	22	0.1	0.04	0.16	1.0	0.06	3	1	59	130	0.1	–
698 saithe (coley)	0.0	0.0	4	0	0.4	0.15	0.20	5.7	0.29	–	0	86	9	0.3	36
699 salad cream	0.0	0.0	12	17	10.5	–	–	–	0.03	3	0	1040	18	0.5	11
700 salad cream, reduced calorie	0.0	0.0	–	–	–	–	–	–	–	–	0	–	–	–	–
701 salami	0.1	0.1	0	0	0.3	0.21	0.23	8.2	0.15	3	–	1850	10	1.0	15
702 salmon	0.0	0.0	13	0	1.9	0.23	0.13	11.0	0.75	16	0	45	21	0.4	37
703 salmon, canned	0.0	0.0	31	0	1.5	0.02	0.22	10.3	0.21	14	0	440	300	0.8	76
704 salmon, smoked	0.0	0.0	–	0	–	0.16	0.17	13.5	0.28	2	0	1880	19	0.6	–
705 salsify (scozonera)	–	3.2	3	20	–	0.06	0.01	0.4	0.07	57	3	5	42	0.9	–
706 samosa, meat	1.9	1.2	28	–	11.9	0.09	0.05	2.1	0.07	6	1	33	34	0.8	4
707 samosa, vegetable	2.4	1.8	31	–	9.8	0.12	0.02	1.2	0.09	11	4	200	32	0.8	4
708 sapodilla	8.2	–	9	53	–	0.01	0.02	0.2	0.04	–	10	7	27	1.1	–
709 sardines, canned in oil	0.0	0.0	11	0	0.3	0.04	0.36	12.6	0.48	8	0	650	550	2.9	23
710 sardines, canned in tomato	0.0	0.0	33	142	0.5	0.02	0.28	8.8	0.35	13	0	700	460	4.6	–
711 sardines, fresh	0.0	0.0	–	0	0.3	0.00	0.22	10.6	0.39	4	0	120	84	1.4	29
712 satsumas	1.2	0.9	9	53	–	0.06	0.03	0.3	0.05	23	19	3	22	0.1	–
713 sausage roll, flaky pastry	1.5	1.2	128	105	1.3	0.10	0.04	3.2	0.06	4	0	510	66	1.2	8
714 sausage roll, short pastry	1.8	1.4	98	80	1.1	0.11	0.05	3.5	0.07	4	0	530	76	1.3	8
715 sausages, beef	0.7	0.5	0	0	0.4	0.03	0.13	7.1	0.06	2	–	810	48	1.4	7
716 sausages, beef, grilled	0.8	0.7	0	0	0.2	0.00	0.14	8.2	0.07	4	–	1100	73	1.7	–
717 sausages, frankfurters	0.1	0.1	0	0	0.3	0.08	0.12	3.0	0.03	1	0	980	34	1.5	–
718 sausages, low fat	–	1.2	0	0	0.3	0.03	0.11	4.4	0.21	2	–	910	90	0.9	–
719 sausages, low fat, grilled	–	1.5	0	0	0.3	0.00	0.13	5.8	0.11	3	–	1190	130	1.3	–
720 sausages, pork	0.6	0.5	0	0	0.2	0.04	0.12	5.7	0.07	1	–	760	41	1.1	–
721 sausages, pork, grilled	0.7	0.7	0	0	0.2	0.02	0.15	6.8	0.06	3	–	1000	53	1.5	–
722 sausages, saveloys	0.4	–	0	0	0.1	0.14	0.09	3.8	0.06	1	–	890	23	1.5	–
723 scampi, in crumb, fried	1.1	–	0	0	–	0.08	0.05	3.6	0.09	-	0	380	99	1.1	41
724 scones, cheese	1.9	1.6	170	–	1.3	0.14	0.12	3.1	0.09	9	0	760	250	1.1	22
725 scones, fruit	3.6	–	–	–	–	0.24	0.10	2.7	0.05	6	0	710	150	1.5	–
726 scones, plain	2.2	1.9	140	–	1.4	0.16	0.07	2.5	0.09	8	0	770	180	1.3	19
727 scones, wholemeal	5.0	5.2	149	115	2.0	0.22	0.10	4.9	0.23	18	0	730	110	2.3	–
728 scones, wholemeal, fruit	5.2	4.9	120	–	1.9	0.20	0.09	4.5	0.23	17	0	650	110	2.3	–
729 scones, wholemeal, plain	5.0	5.2	130	–	2.0	0.22	0.10	4.9	0.23	18	0	730	110	2.3	–

#	per 100 g	serving	average serving	water	energy	energy	protein	carbohydrates	starch	sugars	fat	saturated	mono-unsaturated	poly-unsaturated	cholesterol
			g	g	kcal	kJ	g	g	g	g	g	%	%	%	mg
730	scorzonera (salsify)		50	83.3	27	113	1.3	10.2	3.5	1.5	0.3	–	–	–	–
731	Scotch egg		120	54.0	251	1051	12.0	13.1	13.1	0.0	17.1	30.3	46.5	23.2	165
732	Scotch pancakes (drop scones)	30		39.1	292	1222	5.8	43.6	34.8	8.9	11.7	36.6	39.3	24.1	61
733	seakale		95	95.6	8	33	1.4	0.6	0.0	0.6	0.0	–	–	–	0
734	semolina pudding, skimmed milk		200	76.0	93	389	4.0	20.1	9.3	10.9	0.2	–	–	–	2
735	semolina pudding, whole milk	200		72.4	129	540	3.9	19.9	9.3	10.7	4.3	65.9	29.3	4.9	15
736	sesame seeds	1 tablespoon	10	4.6	598	2503	18.2	0.9	0.5	0.4	58.0	15.0	39.1	45.9	0
737	shaddock (pomelo)	half	125	55.0	18	75	0.4	4.1	0.0	4.1	0.1	–	–	–	0
738	sharon fruit (kaki, persimmon)		110	79.9	73	306	0.8	18.6	0.0	18.6	0.0	–	–	–	0
739	sherry, dry	1 glass	50	81.0	116	486	0.2	1.4	0.0	1.4	0.0	–	–	–	0
740	sherry, medium	1 glass	50	80.5	118	494	0.1	3.6	0.0	3.6	0.0	–	–	–	0
741	sherry, sweet	1 glass	50	74.8	136	569	0.3	6.9	0.0	6.9	0.0	–	–	–	0
742	Shredded Wheat breakfast cereal	2 biscuits	45	7.6	325	1360	10.6	68.3	67.5	0.8	3.0	18.2	18.2	63.6	0
743	Shreddies breakfast cereal		45	4.0	331	1386	10.0	74.1	63.9	10.2	1.5	18.2	18.2	63.6	0
744	shrimps, boiled		50	81.2	73	306	16.5	0.0	0.0	0.0	0.8	16.7	33.3	50.0	200
745	skate		150	80.7	64	268	15.1	0.0	0.0	0.0	0.4	–	–	–	–
746	skate, battered, fried		200	50.7	163	682	14.7	4.0	3.9	0.1	9.9	11.1	37.8	51.1	–
747	Smarties, M and Ms	tube	37	1.5	456	1909	5.4	73.9	3.1	70.8	17.5	62.4	33.9	3.6	17
748	smatana	1 tablespoon	45	–	130	544	4.7	5.6	0.0	5.6	10.0	66.3	30.5	3.2	27
749	soup, chicken, canned	1/2 can	210	87.9	58	243	1.7	4.5	3.4	1.1	3.8	–	–	–	–
750	soup, mushroom, canned	1/2 can	210	89.2	53	222	1.1	3.9	3.1	0.8	3.8	–	–	–	–
751	soup, tomato, canned	1/2 can	210	84.2	55	230	0.8	5.9	3.3	2.6	3.3	–	–	–	–
752	soup, vegetable, canned	1/2 can	210	86.4	37	155	1.5	6.7	4.2	2.5	0.7	–	–	–	–
753	soy sauce	1 teaspoon	5	67.6	64	268	8.7	8.3	–	–	0.0	–	–	–	0
754	soya flour, full fat		–	7.0	447	1871	36.8	23.5	12.3	11.2	23.5	15.4	23.9	60.6	0
755	soya flour, low fat		–	7.0	352	1473	45.3	28.2	14.8	13.4	7.2	15.5	24.1	60.3	0
756	spaghetti, canned in tomato sauce		125	81.9	64	268	1.9	14.1	8.6	5.5	0.4	25.0	25.0	50.0	0
757	spaghetti, white boiled	medium	230	73.8	104	435	3.6	22.2	21.7	0.5	0.7	16.7	16.7	66.7	0
758	spaghetti, white raw		30	9.8	342	1432	12.0	74.1	70.8	3.3	1.8	16.7	16.7	66.7	0
759	spaghetti, wholemeal boiled	medium	230	69.1	113	473	4.7	23.2	21.9	1.3	0.9	22.2	16.7	61.1	0
760	spaghetti, wholemeal, raw		30	10.5	324	1356	13.4	66.2	62.5	3.7	2.5	22.2	16.7	61.1	0
761	Special K breakfast cereal		20	2.7	380	1591	15.3	82.5	64.5	18.0	1.0	33.3	22.2	44.4	0

per 100 g	fibre	non-starch polysaccharide	vit A	carotene	vit E	vit B₁	vit B₂	niacin	vit B₆	folate	vit C	sodium	calcium	iron	iodine
	g	g	µg	µg	mg	mg	mg	mg	mg	µg	mg	mg	mg	mg	µg
730 scorzonera (salsify)	–	3.2	3	20	–	0.06	0.01	0.4	0.07	57	3	5	42	0.9	–
731 Scotch egg	1.6	–	30	0	–	0.08	0.21	3.9	0.13	42	0	670	50	1.8	17
732 Scotch pancakes (drop scones)	1.6	1.4	120	–	1.1	0.13	0.09	2.0	0.08	6	0	430	120	1.0	18
733 seakale	1.1	–	–	–	–	0.06	–	–	–	–	18	4	48	0.6	–
734 semolina pudding, skimmed milk	0.2	0.1	1	0	0.0	0.04	0.17	1.0	0.06	3	1	59	130	0.1	–
735 semolina pudding, whole milk	0.2	0.1	60	22	0.1	0.04	0.16	1.0	0.06	3	1	59	130	0.1	–
736 sesame seeds	–	7.9	1	6	2.5	0.93	0.17	10.4	0.75	97	0	20	670	10.4	–
737 shaddock (pomelo)	0.5	–	2	14	0.1	0.03	0.02	0.2	0.02	16	27	1	16	0.2	–
738 sharon fruit (kaki, persimmon)	–	1.6	158	950	–	0.03	0.05	0.3	–	7	19	5	10	0.1	–
739 sherry, dry	0.0	0.0	0	0	0.0	0.00	0.01	0.1	0.01	0	0	10	7	0.4	–
740 sherry, medium	0.0	0.0	0	0	0.0	0.00	0.01	0.1	0.01	0	0	6	9	0.5	–
741 sherry, sweet	0.0	0.0	0	0	0.0	0.00	0.01	0.1	0.01	0	0	13	7	0.4	–
742 Shredded Wheat breakfast cereal	10.1	9.8	0	0	1.2	0.27	0.05	6.6	0.24	29	0	8	38	4.2	–
743 Shreddies breakfast cereal	10.9	9.5	0	0	–	1.20	2.20	23.1	0.64	28	0	550	40	2.8	–
744 shrimps, boiled	0.0	0.0	–	0	–	0.00	0.02	3.6	–	14	0	375	128	2.6	–
745 skate	0.0	0.0	–	0	–	0.12	0.20	4.8	0.37	–	0	120	40	0.5	20
746 skate, battered, fried	0.2	0.2	7	0	1.0	0.02	0.08	–	–	–	0	110	40	0.8	–
747 Smarties, M and Ms	0.0	0.0	5	28	0.8	0.08	0.79	2.0	0.03	10	0	58	150	1.5	–
748 smatana	0.0	0.0	176	65	0.2	–	–	–	–	–	1	–	–	–	–
749 soup, chicken, canned	1.1	–	0	0	–	0.01	0.03	0.5	0.01	120	0	460	27	0.4	16
750 soup, mushroom, canned	–	–	0	0	–	0.00	0.05	0.5	0.01	–	0	470	30	0.3	16
751 soup, tomato, canned	–	–	35	210	0.0	0.03	0.02	0.6	0.06	12	0	460	17	0.4	16
752 soup, vegetable, canned	–	1.5	2	18	–	0.03	0.02	0.6	0.05	10	0	500	17	0.6	16
753 soy sauce	0.0	0.0	0	0	–	0.05	0.13	4.8	–	11	0	5720	19	2.7	–
754 soya flour, full fat	10.7	11.2	0	0	1.5	0.75	0.28	10.6	0.46	345	0	9	210	6.9	–
755 soya flour, low fat	13.3	13.5	0	0	–	0.90	0.29	13.0	0.52	410	0	14	240	9.1	–
756 spaghetti, canned in tomato sauce	2.8	0.7	–	–	–	0.07	0.01	1.0	0.07	5	0	420	12	0.3	–
757 spaghetti, white boiled	1.8	1.2	0	0	0.0	0.01	0.01	1.2	0.02	4	0	0	7	0.5	0
758 spaghetti, white raw	5.1	2.9	0	0	0.0	0.22	0.03	5.6	0.17	34	0	3	25	2.1	0
759 spaghetti, wholemeal boiled	4.0	3.5	0	0	0.0	0.21	0.02	2.3	0.08	7	0	45	11	1.4	–
760 spaghetti, wholemeal, raw	11.5	8.4	0	0	0.0	0.99	0.11	8.9	0.39	40	0	130	31	3.9	–
761 Special K breakfast cereal	2.7	2.0	0	0	0.6	1.20	1.70	21.1	2.20	300	0	1150	70	13.3	–

	average serving	water	energy	energy	protein	carbohydrates	starch	sugars	fat	saturated	mono-unsaturated	poly-unsaturated	cholesterol
per 100 g	g	g	kcal	kJ	g	g	g	g	g	%	%	%	mg
762 spinach	95	91.8	19	80	2.2	0.8	0.0	0.8	0.8	14.3	14.3	71.4	0
763 spirits (40% alcohol by volume) single	25	68.3	222	929	0.0	0.0	0.0	0.0	0.0	–	–	–	0
764 sponge pudding	95	32.8	340	1423	5.8	45.3	26.4	18.9	16.3	32.7	41.0	26.3	92
765 sprats	80	66.3	172	720	18.3	0.0	0.0	0.0	11.0	22.2	47.5	30.3	93
766 spring greens	95	92.2	20	84	1.9	1.6	0.2	1.4	0.7	16.7	16.7	66.7	0
767 spring onions 2 onions	20	92.2	23	96	2.0	3.0	0.2	2.8	0.5	25.0	25.0	50.0	0
768 squash, acorn	65	82.9	56	234	1.1	12.6	10.8	1.6	0.1	–	–	–	0
769 squash, butternut	65	87.8	32	134	0.9	7.4	3.0	3.9	0.1	–	–	–	0
770 squash, spaghetti	65	92.3	23	96	0.7	4.3	0.6	3.4	0.3	–	–	–	0
771 squid	65	80.5	81	339	15.4	1.2	0.0	0.0	1.7	33.3	16.7	50.0	225
772 squid, battered, fried	120	62.4	195	816	11.5	15.7	12.9	2.2	10.0	–	–	–	–
773 starfruit (carambola, star apple)	15	91.4	32	134	0.5	7.3	0.2	7.1	0.3	–	–	–	0
774 Start breakfast cereal	20	3.0	354	1482	7.9	82.0	50.5	31.5	1.7	21.4	28.6	50.0	0
775 steak and kidney pie individual	160	42.6	323	1352	9.1	25.6	23.3	2.3	21.2	41.6	48.0	10.4	36
776 strawberries	100	89.5	27	113	0.8	6.0	0.0	6.0	0.1	–	–	–	0
777 suet pudding	90	36.0	335	1402	4.4	40.5	26.3	14.2	18.3	58.4	39.1	2.6	82
778 suet, shredded	–	1.5	826	3458	0.0	12.1	11.9	0.2	86.7	58.4	39.1	2.6	82
779 sugar 1 tsp	5	0.0	394	1649	0.0	100.0	0.0	0.0	0.0	–	–	–	0
780 sugar apple (custard apple, sweetsop)	–	73.2	69	289	1.6	16.1	1.2	14.9	0.3	–	–	–	0
781 Sugar Puffs breakfast cereal	20	1.8	324	1356	5.9	84.5	28.0	56.5	0.8	16.7	16.7	66.7	0
782 Sultana Bran breakfast cereal	30	7.0	302	1264	8.5	67.7	34.9	32.9	1.6	23.5	17.6	58.8	0
783 sultanas 1 tablespoon	30	15.2	275	1151	2.7	69.4	0.0	69.4	0.4	–	–	–	–
784 sunflower seeds 1 tablespoon	15	4.4	581	2432	19.8	18.6	16.3	1.7	47.5	9.9	21.6	68.4	0
785 swede	60	95.8	11	46	0.3	2.3	0.1	2.2	0.1	–	–	–	0
786 sweet potato, baked	130	65.6	115	481	1.6	27.9	13.4	14.5	0.4	–	–	–	0
787 sweet potato, boiled	130	74.7	84	352	1.1	20.5	8.9	11.6	0.3	–	–	–	0
788 sweetbread, lamb	–	75.5	131	548	15.3	0.0	0.0	0.0	7.8	52.6	42.1	5.3	260
789 sweetcorn (maize) 1 cob	210	41.2	66	276	2.5	11.6	10.0	1.4	1.4	20.0	30.0	50.0	0
790 sweets, boiled each	5	0.0	327	1369	0.0	87.3	0.4	86.9	0.0	–	–	–	0
791 sweetsop (custard apple, sugar apple)	–	73.2	69	289	1.6	16.1	1.2	14.9	0.3	–	–	–	0
792 Swiss chard	90	92.7	20	84	1.9	3.2	2.8	0.4	0.1	–	–	–	0
793 swordfish	140	80.8	109	456	18.0	0.0	0.0	0.0	4.1	25.0	44.4	30.6	41

per 100 g	fibre	non-starch polysaccharide	vit A	carotene	vit E	vit B$_1$	vit B$_2$	niacin	vit B$_6$	folate	vit C	sodium	calcium	iron	iodine
	g	g	µg	µg	mg	mg	mg	mg	mg	µg	mg	mg	mg	mg	µg
762 spinach	3.1	2.1	640	3840	1.7	0.06	0.05	1.5	0.09	90	8	120	160	1.6	2
763 spirits (40% alcohol by volume)	0.0	0.0	0	0	0.0	0.00	0.00	0.0	0.00	0	0	0	0	0.0	0
764 sponge pudding	1.2	1.1	192	130	1.8	0.09	0.09	2.0	0.06	8	0	310	84	1.1	19
765 sprats	0.0	0.0	60	0	0.5	0.00	0.20	6.4	0.27	–	0	200	97	1.1	64
766 spring greens	3.4	2.6	378	2270	–	0.05	0.06	1.5	0.18	66	77	10	75	1.4	–
767 spring onions	–	1.5	103	620	–	0.05	0.03	1.0	0.13	54	26	7	39	1.9	–
768 squash, acorn	–	3.2	43	260	–	0.17	0.01	1.2	0.19	19	11	4	44	0.9	–
769 squash, butternut	–	1.4	543	3255	1.8	0.07	0.02	0.8	0.12	19	15	4	41	0.6	–
770 squash, spaghetti	–	2.1	11	66	–	0.04	0.02	1.0	0.10	8	3	18	21	0.3	–
771 squid	0.0	0.0	15	0	1.2	0.10	0.12	6.7	0.69	13	0	110	13	0.5	20
772 squid, battered, fried	0.6	0.5	48	13	2.4	0.10	0.13	4.1	0.32	15	0	88	81	0.7	19
773 starfruit (carambola, star apple)	1.7	1.3	6	37	–	0.03	0.03	0.4	–	–	31	2	5	0.6	–
774 Start breakfast cereal	9.3	5.7	0	0	18.7	1.50	2.20	25.1	2.70	400	38	410	68	15.0	–
775 steak and kidney pie	1.0	0.9	–	0	–	0.12	0.15	3.4	0.06	8	0	510	53	2.5	–
776 strawberries	2.0	1.1	1	8	0.2	0.03	0.03	0.7	0.06	20	77	6	16	0.4	9
777 suet pudding	1.4	0.9	30	–	0.1	0.09	0.06	1.5	0.04	5	0	420	96	0.7	11
778 suet, shredded	0.6	0.5	64	73	1.5	0.00	0.00	0.0	0.00	0	0	0	0	0.0	5
779 sugar	0.0	0.0	0	0	0.0	0.00	0.00	0.0	0.00	0	0	0	0	0.0	0
780 sugar apple (custard apple, sweetsop)	–	–	1	4	–	0.11	0.11	0.9	0.20	–	36	7	21	0.6	–
781 Sugar Puffs breakfast cereal	4.8	3.2	0	0	0.3	0.00	0.03	3.7	0.05	12	0	9	14	2.1	–
782 Sultana Bran breakfast cereal	15.5	10.0	0	0	–	1.00	1.50	18.0	1.80	250	–	610	51	30.0	–
783 sultanas	6.3	2.0	2	12	0.7	0.09	0.05	1.0	0.25	27	0	19	64	2.2	–
784 sunflower seeds	–	6.0	3	15	37.8	1.60	0.19	9.1	–	–	0	3	110	6.4	–
785 swede	1.2	0.7	28	165	0.0	0.13	0.01	1.1	0.04	18	15	14	26	0.1	–
786 sweet potato, baked	3.0	3.3	857	5140	6.0	0.09	0.00	0.8	0.07	9	23	52	31	0.9	3
787 sweet potato, boiled	2.1	2.3	660	3960	4.4	0.07	0.01	0.8	0.05	8	17	32	23	0.7	2
788 sweetbread, lamb	0.0	0.0	0	0	0.4	0.03	0.25	7.0	0.03	13	18	75	8	1.7	–
789 sweetcorn (maize)	2.5	1.3	12	71	0.5	0.11	0.03	1.5	0.09	20	4	1	2	0.3	–
790 sweets, boiled	0.0	0.0	0	0	0.0	0.00	0.00	0.0	0.00	0	0	25	5	0.4	–
791 sweetsop (custard apple, sugar apple)	–	–	1	4	–	0.11	0.11	0.9	0.20	–	36	7	21	0.6-	
792 Swiss chard	–	–	728	4365	–	0.03	0.09	0.7	–	100	18	180	58	2.3	–
793 swordfish	0.0	0.0	–	0	–	0.16	0.17	11.7	0.51	–	0	130	4	0.5	–

per 100 g		average serving	water	energy	energy	protein	carbohydrates	starch	sugars	fat	saturated	mono-unsaturated	poly-unsaturated	cholesterol
		g	g	kcal	kJ	g	g	g	g	g	%	%	%	mg
794 syrup, golden		15	20.0	298	1247	0.3	79.0	0.0	79.0	0.0	–	–	–	0
795 tamarillos (tree tomatoes)		–	86.5	28	117	2.0	4.7	0.0	4.7	0.3	–	–	–	0
796 tamarind		–	35.8	238	996	2.3	56.5	–	–	0.3	–	–	–	0
797 tangerines		95	63.3	25	105	0.7	5.8	0.0	5.8	0.1	–	–	–	0
798 tannia		130	70.5	107	448	1.3	24.5	24.3	0.2	0.4	–	–	–	0
799 tapioca		–	12.2	359	1503	0.4	95.0	95.0	0.0	0.1	–	–	–	0
800 taramasalata	small tub	100	35.9	446	1867	3.2	4.1	4.1	0.0	46.4	8.3	58.5	33.2	37
801 taro		130	72.9	91	381	1.2	22.4	21.5	0.9	0.2	–	–	–	0
802 taro leaves		95	92.1	19	80	2.4	1.4	0.2	1.2	0.5	–	–	–	0
803 teacakes, toasted	1	60	18.6	329	1377	8.9	58.3	41.9	16.4	8.3	–	–	–	20
804 tempeh (fermented soya bean cake)		–	61.0	166	695	20.7	6.4	4.6	0.9	6.4	15.3	24.5	60.2	0
805 tigernuts (chuffa)		–	8.5	403	1687	4.3	45.7	29.6	16.1	23.8	17.7	72.6	9.7	0
806 toffees, mixed	each	8	4.8	430	1800	2.1	71.1	1.0	70.1	17.2	85.1	13.7	1.2	17
807 tofu (soya bean curd), steamed	60	85.0	73	306	8.1	0.7	0.3	0.3	4.2	15.2	24.2	60.6	0	
808 tomato juice		110	93.8	14	59	0.8	3.0	0.0	3.0	0.0	–	–	–	0
809 tomato ketchup	1 portion pack	20	64.8	98	410	2.1	24.0	1.1	22.9	0.0	–	–	–	0
810 tomatoes	1 medium	85	93.1	17	71	0.7	3.1	0.0	3.1	0.3	25.0	25.0	50.0	0
811 tongue, pickled	2 slices	50	48.6	293	1226	19.5	0.0	5.6	0.0	23.9	–	–	–	100
812 tortilla chips		50	0.9	459	1921	7.6	60.1	58.9	1.2	22.6	18.8	49.8	31.5	0
813 trail mix		30	8.9	432	1808	9.1	37.2	0.1	37.1	28.5	–	–	–	0
814 treacle tart		70	21.4	368	1540	3.7	60.4	26.8	33.6	14.1	37.8	43.0	19.3	19
815 treacle, black		15	28.5	257	1076	1.2	67.2	0.0	67.2	0.0	–	–	–	0
816 tree tomatoes (tamarillos)		50	86.5	28	117	2.0	4.7	0.0	4.7	0.3	–	–	–	0
817 tripe, stewed		150	78.5	100	419	14.8	0.0	0.0	0.0	4.5	63.2	34.2	2.6	160
818 trout	whole fish	230	76.7	125	523	19.6	0.0	0.0	0.0	5.2	23.9	39.1	37.0	67
819 tuna		120	70.4	136	569	23.7	0.0	0.0	0.0	4.6	30.0	30.0	40.0	28
820 tuna, canned in brine		100	74.6	99	414	23.5	0.0	0.0	0.0	0.6	30.0	30.0	40.0	51
821 tuna, canned in oil		100	63.3	189	791	27.1	0.0	0.0	0.0	9.0	17.3	27.2	55.6	50
822 turbot		150	78.7	95	398	17.7	0.0	0.0	0.0	2.7	36.8	31.6	31.6	–
823 turkey, roast, dark meat		90	67.7	148	620	27.8	0.0	0.0	0.0	4.1	34.2	44.7	21.1	100
824 turkey, roast, light meat		90	68.4	132	553	29.8	0.0	0.0	0.0	1.4	30.8	46.2	23.1	62
825 turkey, roast, meat and skin		90	65.0	171	716	28.0	0.0	0.0	0.0	6.5	34.4	44.3	21.3	191
826 turkey, roast, meat only		90	68.0	140	586	28.8	0.0	0.0	0.0	2.7	36.0	44.0	20.0	79

per 100 g	fibre	non-starch polysaccharide	vit A	carotene	vit E	vit B₁	vit B₂	niacin	vit B₆	folate	vit C	sodium	calcium	iron	iodine
	g	g	µg	µg	mg	mg	mg	mg	mg	µg	mg	mg	mg	mg	µg
794 syrup, golden	0.0	0.0	0	0	0.0	0.00	0.00	0.0	0.00	0	0	270	26	1.5	0
795 tamarillos (tree tomatoes)	–	–	153	920	1.9	0.06	0.03	0.6	0.19	–	23	1	10	0.8	–
796 tamarind	–	–	2	14	–	0.29	0.10	1.4	0.08	–	3	15	77	1.8	–
797 tangerines	1.2	0.9	12	71	–	0.05	0.01	0.2	0.05	15	22	1	31	0.2	–
798 tannia	–	2.3	5	29	–	0.02	0.05	0.6	–	–	16	4	14	0.6	–
799 tapioca		0.4	0	0	0.0	0.00	0.00	0.1	0.00	0	0	4	8	0.3	–
800 taramasalata	–	–	–	–	–	0.08	0.10	0.9	–	4	1	650	21	0.4	–
801 taro	3.0	2.1	5	32	–	0.05	0.02	0.8	0.05	–	7	3	27	0.8	–
802 taro leaves	2.2	–	638	3830	–	0.14	0.38	1.7	–	27	35	2	86	1.2	–
803 teacakes, toasted	4.7	–	–	–	–	0.20	0.17	3.8	0.06	40	0	300	98	2.9	–
804 tempeh (fermented soya bean cake)	4.1	4.3	5	30	–	0.19	0.48	7.9	1.86	76	0	6	120	3.6	–
805 tigernuts (chuffa)	17.4	11.7	0	0	–	0.23	0.10	1.8	–	–	6	1	48	3.2	–
806 toffees, mixed	0.0	0.0	–	–	–	0.00	0.00	0.4	0.00	0	0	320	95	1.5	–
807 tofu (soya bean curd), steamed	0.3	–	0	2	1.0	0.06	0.02	1.4	0.07	15	0	4	510	1.2	–
808 tomato juice	–	0.6	33	200	1.0	0.02	0.02	0.8	0.06	10	8	230	10	0.4	2
809 tomato ketchup	–	0.9	38	230	–	1.00	0.09	2.4	0.03	1	2	1120	25	1.2	–
810 tomatoes	1.3	1.0	107	640	1.2	0.09	0.01	1.1	0.14	17	17	9	7	0.5	2
811 tongue, pickled	1.3	0.0	0	0	0.4	0.06	0.29	8.3	0.09	5	2	1000	31	3.0	–
812 tortilla chips	–	4.9	76	455	1.9	0.17	0.09	2.6	0.31	–	0	850	150	1.6	–
813 trail mix	–	4.3	8	47	4.5	0.23	0.09	3.5	–	25	0	27	69	3.7	–
814 treacle tart	1.4	1.1	68	57	0.7	0.08	0.01	1.3	0.04	4	0	360	62	1.4	–
815 treacle, black	0.0	0.0	0	0	0.0	0.00	0.00	0.0	0.00	0	0	96	500	9.2	0
816 tree tomatoes (tamarillos)	–	–	153	920	1.9	0.06	0.03	0.6	0.19	–	23	1	10	0.8	–
817 tripe, stewed	0.0	0.0	0	0	0.1	0.00	0.08	3.2	0.02	1	3	73	150	0.7	–
818 trout	0.0	0.0	49	0	0.7	0.20	0.11	8.2	0.34	9	0	45	18	0.3	13
819 tuna	0.0	0.0	26	0	–	0.10	0.13	17.2	0.38	15	0	47	16	1.3	30
820 tuna, canned in brine	0.0	0.0	–	0	0.6	0.02	0.11	18.8	0.47	16	0	320	8	1.0	13
821 tuna, canned in oil	0.0	0.0	–	0	–	0.02	0.12	21.1	0.51	–	0	290	12	1.6	14
822 turbot	0.0	0.0	0	0	–	0.05	0.11	5.4	–	–	0	68	49	0.5	–
823 turkey, roast, dark meat	0.0	0.0	0	0	0.0	0.07	0.29	11.9	0.32	17	0	71	12	1.4	–
824 turkey, roast, light meat	0.0	0.0	0	0	0.0	0.07	0.14	15.6	0.31	13	0	45	7	0.5	–
825 turkey, roast, meat and skin	0.0	0.0	0	0	–	–	–	–	–	–	0	52	9	0.9	–
826 turkey, roast, meat only	0.0	0.0	0	0	0.0	0.07	0.21	13.9	0.32	15	0	57	9	0.9	–

per 100 g		average serving g	water g	energy kcal	energy kJ	protein g	carbohydrates g	starch g	sugars g	fat g	saturated %	mono-unsaturated %	poly-unsaturated %	cholesterol mg
827 Turkish delight	1 square	15	16.1	295	1235	0.6	77.9	9.3	68.6	0.0	–	–	–	0
828 turnip		60	93.1	12	50	0.6	2.0	0.1	1.9	0.2	–	–	–	0
829 turnip tops		95	92.8	13	54	2.7	0.2	0.1	0.1	0.0	–	–	–	0
830 Twiglets		25	3.2	383	1603	11.3	62.0	60.9	1.1	11.7	44.1	39.6	16.2	0
831 Twix	standard bar	56	3.5	480	2009	5.6	63.2	15.5	47.7	24.5	51.9	41.1	6.9	–
832 veal, fillet, roast		150	55.1	230	963	31.6	0.0	0.0	0.0	11.5	35.6	47.1	17.3	155
833 venison, roast		120	56.8	198	829	35.0	0.0	0.0	0.0	6.4	–	–	–	–
834 walnuts, shelled	3 nuts	20	2.8	688	2880	14.7	3.3	0.7	2.6	68.5	8.5	18.9	72.5	0
835 watercress	1/4 bunch	20	92.5	22	92	3.0	0.4	0.0	0.4	1.0	37.5	12.5	50.0	0
836 Weetabix breakfast cereal	2 biscuits	40	5.8	354	1482	10.7	78.3	71.9	6.4	2.0	20.0	20.0	60.0	0
837 Weetaflake breakfast cereal		20	5.8	342	1432	10.7	74.9	68.5	6.4	2.0	19.0	19.0	61.9	0
838 Weetaflake 'n' raisin breakfast cereal		20	8.0	337	1411	8.2	79.8	55.2	24.6	0.6	–	–	–	0
839 Weetos breakfast cereal		20	3.0	341	1427	8.2	80.5	51.1	29.4	0.7	31.6	0.0	68.4	0
840 whelks, weighed with shell		200	11.6	14	59	2.8	0.0	0.0	0.0	0.3	33.3	33.3	33.3	19
841 whitebait, floured and fried		80	23.5	525	2198	19.5	5.3	5.2	0.1	47.5	–	–	–	–
842 whiting		150	80.7	81	339	18.7	0.0	0.0	0.0	0.7	20.0	40.0	40.0	46
843 whiting, in crumbs, fried		120	56.8	173	724	16.3	6.3	6.1	0.2	9.3	10.7	38.1	51.2	–
844 wine, red		125	90.3	68	285	0.2	0.3	0.0	0.3	0.0	–	–	–	0
845 wine, white, dry		125	89.1	66	276	0.1	0.6	0.0	0.6	0.0	–	–	–	0
846 wine, white, sweet		125	80.6	94	393	0.2	5.9	0.0	5.9	0.0	–	–	–	0
847 winkles, weighed with shell		–	15.1	14	59	2.9	0.0	0.0	0.0	0.3	–	–	–	20
848 yam		130	64.4	133	557	1.7	33.0	32.3	0.7	0.3	–	–	–	0
849 yogurt, full cream, fruit	small pot	60	73.1	105	440	5.1	15.7	0.0	15.7	2.8	60.0	32.0	8.0	10
850 yogurt, full cream, plain	small pot	60	81.9	79	331	5.7	7.8	0.0	7.8	3.0	60.7	32.1	7.1	11
851 yogurt, Greek, cows	1/2 medium pot	100	78.5	115	481	6.4	2.0	0.0	2.0	9.1	61.9	32.1	6.0	–
852 yogurt, Greek, sheep	1/2 medium pot	100	80.9	106	444	4.4	5.6	0.0	5.6	7.5	67.6	26.8	5.6	14
853 yogurt, low fat, flavoured	small pot	60	77.9	90	377	3.8	17.9	0.0	17.9	0.9	55.6	33.3	11.1	4
854 yogurt, low fat, plain	small pot	60	84.9	56	234	5.1	7.5	0.0	7.5	0.8	71.4	28.6	0.0	4
855 yogurt, low fat, with fruit	small pot	60	77.0	90	377	4.1	17.9	0.0	17.9	0.7	66.7	33.3	0.0	4
856 Yorkshire pudding		80	57.4	208	871	6.6	24.7	21.0	3.7	9.9	55.8	37.9	6.3	68

per 100 g	fibre	non-starch polysaccharide	vit A	carotene	vit E	vit B$_1$	vit B$_2$	niacin	vit B$_6$	folate	vit C	sodium	calcium	iron	iodine
	g	g	µg	µg	mg	mg	mg	mg	mg	µg	mg	mg	mg	mg	µg
827 Turkish delight	0.0	0.0	0	0	0.0	0.13	–	–	–	–	0	31	10	0.2	0
828 turnip	2.0	1.9	3	20	0.0	0.05	0.02	0.3	0.04	8	10	28	45	0.2	–
829 turnip tops	3.5	–	1000	6000	2.9	0.06	0.20	1.1	0.18	120	40	7	98	3.1	–
830 Twiglets	–	10.3	0	0	2.5	0.37	0.48	10.1	0.38	–	0	1330	45	2.9	–
831 Twix	–	–	1	7	3.7	0.06	0.22	1.5	0.05	–	0	190	110	1.1	–
832 veal, fillet, roast	0.0	0.0	0	0	–	0.06	0.27	13.7	0.32	4	0	97	14	1.6	–
833 venison, roast	0.0	0.0	–	–	–	0.22	0.69	12.0	0.65	6	0	86	29	7.8	–
834 walnuts, shelled	5.9	3.5	0	0	3.9	0.40	0.14	4.0	0.67	66	0	7	94	2.9	9
835 watercress	3.0	1.5	420	2520	1.5	0.16	0.06	0.8	0.23	–	62	49	170	2.2	–
836 Weetabix breakfast cereal	8.5	9.7	0	0	1.0	0.70	1.00	12.1	0.22	50	0	370	35	6.0	–
837 Weetaflake breakfast cereal	11.6	9.7	0	0	1.0	0.20	1.00	12.1	0.22	50	0	370	35	6.0	–
838 Weetaflake 'n' raisin breakfast cereal	7.2	–	0	0	–	0.60	1.30	11.2	–	–	1	200	77	7.0-	
839 Weetos breakfast cereal	11.7	–	7	–	0.0	1.00	1.50	17.6	0.00	2	30	830	65	10.0	–
840 whelks, weighed with shell	0.0	0.0	–	0	0.1	0.01	0.03	0.8	0.01	–	0	40	8	0.9	–
841 whitebait, floured and fried	0.2	0.2	–	0	–	–	–	–	–	–	–	230	860	5.1	–
842 whiting	0.0	0.0	0	0	–	0.05	0.26	5.2	0.17	–	0	90	18	0.1	67
843 whiting, in crumbs, fried	0.3	0.3	0	0	–	–	–	–	–	–	0	180	43	0.6	–
844 wine, red	0.0	0.0	0	0	0.0	0.00	0.02	0.1	0.02	0	0	10	7	0.9	–
845 wine, white, dry	0.0	0.0	0	0	0.0	0.00	0.01	0.1	0.02	0	0	4	9	0.5	–
846 wine, white, sweet	0.0	0.0	0	0	0.0	0.00	0.01	0.1	0.01	0	0	13	14	0.6	–
847 winkles, weighed with shell	0.0	0.0	–	0	–	0.05	0.07	0.9	0.02	–	0	220	26	2.9	–
848 yam	3.5	1.4	0	0	–	0.14	0.01	0.6	0.12	6	4	17	12	0.4	–
849 yogurt, full cream, fruit	–	–	42	16	0.1	0.06	0.30	1.4	0.07	10	1	82	160	0.0	48
850 yogurt, full cream, plain	0.0	0.0	32	21	0.1	0.06	0.27	1.5	0.10	18	1	80	200	0.1	63
851 yogurt, Greek, cows	0.0	0.0	121	36	0.4	0.03	0.36	1.6	0.05	6	0	71	150	0.3	–
852 yogurt, Greek, sheep	0.0	0.0	88	11	0.7	0.05	0.33	1.2	0.08	3	0	150	150	0.0	–
853 yogurt, low fat, flavoured	0.0	0.0	10	6	0.0	0.05	0.21	1.0	0.07	19	1	65	150	0.1	–
854 yogurt, low fat, plain	0.0	0.0	9	5	0.0	0.05	0.25	1.3	0.09	17	1	83	190	0.1	63
855 yogurt, low fat, with fruit	–	–	11	4	0.0	0.05	0.21	1.1	0.08	16	1	64	150	0.1	48
856 Yorkshire pudding	1.0	0.9	66	14	0.4	0.10	0.16	2.1	0.07	9	1	590	130	0.9	27

per 100 g	average serving g	water g	energy kcal	energy kJ	protein g	carbohydrates g	starch g	sugars g	fat g	saturated %	mono-unsaturated %	poly-unsaturated %	cholesterol mg

per 100 g	fibre	non-starch polysaccharide	vit A	carotene	vit E	vit B$_1$	vit B$_2$	niacin	vit B$_6$	folate	vit C	sodium	calcium	iron	iodine
	g	g	µg	µg	mg	mg	mg	mg	mg	µg	mg	mg	mg	mg	µg

Table 23 Foods that are sources of vitamin D – micrograms of vitamin D/100 g of food (numbers are as in Table 22; see Table 22 for average portion sizes)

no		µg	no		µg
2	All-Bran breakfast cereal	2.8	255	cream, whipping	0.2
80	bloater, grilled	16.2	257	creme eggs (Easter eggs)	0.6
85	Bran Buds breakfast cereal	2.8	260	Crunchy Nut Corn Flakes	2.8
86	Bran Flakes breakfast cereal	2.8	266	custard, made with egg	0.4
93	bread, croissant	0.2	274	dogfish (rock salmon)	9.1
100	bread, naan	0.2	281	drop scones (Scotch pancakes)	0.9
125	bun, hot cross	0.6	286	eel (weighed with bones)	4.9
141	butter	0.8	287	eel, jellied	3.0
147	cake, gateau	0.5	288	egg	1.8
150	cake, rich fruit	1.1	290	egg yolk	4.9
151	cake, sponge	2.8	291	egg, duck	5.0
152	cake, sponge, fatless	0.7	293	faggots	0.2
161	cauliflower cheese	0.2	322	Frosties breakfast cereal	2.8
168	cheese spread	0.2	327	Fruit'n Fibre breakfast cereal	2.8
169	cheese, brie	0.2	330	ghee	1.9
170	cheese, camembert	0.2	341	Grapenuts breakfast cereal	4.4
171	cheese, cheddar	0.3	359	herring	19.0
173	cheese, Cheshire	0.2	360	herring, grilled	17.0
177	cheese, cream	0.3	361	herring, pickled	16.0
178	cheese, Danish blue	0.2	364	HoneySmacks	2.8
179	cheese, Derby	0.3	391	kipper, boil in bag	7.9
180	cheese, double Gloucester	0.3	392	kipper, grilled	5.9
181	cheese, Edam	0.2	422	liver sausage	0.6
183	cheese, Feta	0.5	423	liver, calf	0.3
184	cheese, goat	0.5	424	liver, chicken	0.2
185	cheese, Gouda	0.2	425	liver, lamb	0.5
186	cheese, Gruyere	0.3	426	liver, ox	1.1
187	cheese, Lancashire	0.2	427	liver, pork	1.1
188	cheese, Leicester	0.3	435	macaroni cheese	0.4
189	cheese, Parmesan	0.3	438	mackerel	5.0
190	cheese, processed	0.2	439	mackerel, canned in brine	5.6
196	cheese, Stilton	0.3	440	mackerel, canned in tomato	4.7
197	cheese, Wensleydale	0.2	441	mackerel, grilled	5.0
219	Christmas pudding	0.2	442	mackerel, smoked	8.0
224	Coco Pops	2.8	448	margarine, dairy spread	5.8
237	corn flakes	2.8	449	margarine, hard	7.9
250	cream, clotted	0.3	450	margarine, hard, vegetarian	7.9
251	cream, double	0.3	451	margarine, low fat spread	8.0
254	cream, soured	0.2	452	margarine, polyunsaturated	7.9

Table 23 *continued*   (micrograms of vitamin D/100 g of food)

no		µg	no		µg
453	margarine, soft	7.9	694	roe, herring (soft)	4.0
454	margarine, soft, vegetarian	7.9	699	salad cream	0.2
463	mayonnaise, bought	0.3	702	salmon	8.0
464	mayonnaise, home made	0.5	703	salmon, canned	17.0
471	McDonalds Big Mac	0.4	709	sardines, canned in oil	7.5
478	McDonalds Egg McMuffin	0.9	710	sardines, canned in tomato	7.5
480	McDonalds Filet o'Fish	0.4	711	sardines, fresh	11.0
497	McDonalds Quarterpounder cheeseburger	0.3	713	sausage roll, flaky pastry	1.1
498	McDonalds Quarterpounder hamburger	0.3	714	sausage roll, short pastry	0.9
518	milk, calcium fortified	0.2	724	scones, cheese	1.1
520	milk, evaporated	4.0	726	scones, plain	1.2
524	milk, sheep	0.2	727	scones, wholemeal	1.2
536	muffins	0.4	728	scones, wholemeal, fruit	1.0
537	muffins, bran	0.2	729	scones, wholemeal, plain	1.2
548	noodles, egg, raw	0.3	731	Scotch egg	0.7
551	Nutri-Grain breakfast cereal	2.8	732	Scotch pancakes (drop scones)	0.9
574	oysters, weighed without shells	1.0	761	Special K breakfast cereal	2.8
576	pancakes, sweet	0.2	764	sponge pudding	1.6
584	pastry, flaky, baked	1.8	765	sprats	13.0
585	pastry, flaky, raw	1.3	774	Start breakfast cereal	4.2
586	pastry, shortcrust, baked	1.4	782	Sultana Bran breakfast cereal	2.8
587	pastry, shortcrust, raw	1.2	814	treacle tart	0.6
588	pastry, wholemeal, baked	1.4	818	trout	10.6
589	pastry, wholemeal, raw	1.2	819	tuna	7.2
614	pilchards, canned in tomato	8.0	820	tuna, canned in brine	4.0
671	quiche	0.9	821	tuna, canned in oil	5.8
684	Rice Krispies breakfast cereal	2.8	839	Weetos breakfast cereal	2.8
690	Ricicles breakfast cereal	2.8	852	yogurt, Greek, sheep	0.2
691	rock salmon (dogfish)	9.1	856	Yorkshire pudding	0.3
693	roe, cod (hard)	18.0			

D) Alcoholic beverages

There are several different ways of expressing the alcohol content of alcoholic beverages. The old way was by degrees proof – proof spirit was defined in Britain as that concentration of alcohol in water that would burn well enough to ignite gunpowder. Note that the American definition of proof spirit was different, so that a spirit that is 70° proof in Britain would be 80° proof in USA.

Most usually now, the alcohol content is given on labels as percentage by volume (sometimes abbreviated to ABV, meaning alcohol by volume). You may sometimes also see it as percentage by weight. This differs from percentage by volume for two reasons:

- alcohol is lighter than water (it has a density of 0.79 g/ml);
- when alcohol is dissolved in water there is a reduction in volume.

For calculation of the energy yield of alcoholic beverages(see separate entries in Table 22), we need to know the weight of alcohol (g)/100 ml of the beverage, since we drink beverages by volume, and not by weight. Table 24 shows the alcohol content of beverages in all of these different ways.

An alternative way of considering alcohol consumption is to use the unit of alcohol. For public health purposes, a unit of alcohol is defined as 10 ml (8 g) of absolute (pure) alcohol. Table 25 shows the amounts of beverages that provide 1 unit of alcohol, and Table 26 shows the upper limits of prudent alcohol consumption. Note that the upper limits for women are lower than for men – women are more susceptible to the adverse effects of excessive alcohol consumption than men are.

In Europe, in addition to labelling by their alcohol content, white wines are graded as dry (0.6% sugars) to sweet (6% sugars) on a scale of 1 to 9. Red wines are graded from A (light and dry) to E (full bodied and heavy).

Table 24 Alcohol content of beverages

	% by volume	g/100 ml	° proof
beer, cider	4–6	3.2–4.8	10
table wines	9–13	7.1–10.3	20–25
sherry, port, aperitif wines	18–25	14.3–19.5	30–45
liqueurs	20–40	15.9–31.7	35–70
spirits	38–45	30.1–35.7	70
proof spirit, UK	57.07	45.2	100
proof spirit, USA	50	39.6	100

Table 25 The unit of alcohol

1 unit of alcohol =	
	8 g absolute alcohol
	1/2 pint (300 ml) beer or cider
	1 glass (100 ml) of wine
	1 glass (50 ml) sherry or port
	1 single measure (25 ml) of spirit

Table 26 Upper limits of prudent alcohol consumption

	men	women
units/day	4	3
g alcohol/day	32	24
units/week	21	14
g alcohol/week	168	112

E) Food labelling

Food labelling throughout the European Union is strictly regulated by national laws that have to conform to European Commission Directives. The regulations apply to all processed foods ready for delivery to the ultimate consumer, and also to foods sold to caterers, but not to foods intended for immediate consumption where they are bought (i.e. catering establishments and restaurants).

The following information **must** appear on the label:

- The name of the food;

- The amount in the package, in g or ml. Where this is a standard package that has been declared to the appropriate authorities of the EU, the weight or volume may be preceeded by a small letter 'e'.

- A date mark indicating the date up to and including which the food can reasonably be expected to retain its essential properties if stored properly. If special storage conditions are required, these must be stated close to the date mark:

  - For foods with a shelf life of up to 12 weeks the date marking reads 'best before day, month, year';

  - For foods with a shelf life longer than 12 weeks, the date marking reads 'best before month, year';

  - Perishable foods with a shelf life of less than a month may have a 'sell by' or 'display until' date instead, together with advice on how soon after purchase they should be consumed, or a simple 'eat by' or 'use by' date, showing the date after which they may be unfit for consumption, or liable to spoilage. It is illegal to sell a product after these dates;

  - Frozen foods and ice cream carry star markings, which correspond to the star markings on freezers and frozen food compartments of refrigerators (see Table 46).

- A list of the ingredients, in descending order by weight (i.e. the major ingredient must come first). From February 2000 the amount of each ingredient will also have to be shown.

  - Water added to a product must be declared if it constitutes more than 5% by weight of the final product;

  - Additives must be declared, either by name or by number (see Table 30);

  - Certain foods do not have to bear a list of ingredients: these include fresh fruit and vegetables, fortified flour, foods consisting of a single ingredient, foods with a legally defined composition, such as margarine, and certain fermented foods with no added ingredients other than enzymes and cultures used to ferment them;

- Any special storage or cooking conditions;

- The name and address of the manufacturer, packager or importer.

In addition, most packages now have a machine-readable bar code (a universal product code), which identifies the product and package size, manufacturer and nature of the contents. This permits automated stock keeping and supermarket checkouts.

Claims and misleading descriptions

It is an offence to label or advertise a food so as to describe it falsely, or to mislead as to its nature, substance or quality (including nutritional value). There are specific regulations concerning claims for energy, calories, protein, vitamins and minerals, as well as claims that a food is beneficial for slimming, or has any tonic, restorative or medicinal properties. It is illegal to mislead the consumer even if the claim is technically a true statement.

Any food that has been specially manufactured to meet the requirements of a particular group of people (e.g. babies, people with diabetes, etc.) must carry on its label an indication of its special nutritional characteristics and the particular aspects of its composition, or the manufacturing process, which makes it suitable for the intended consumer.

Other foods may be labelled as 'suitable for vegetarians' implying that they do not contain any products of animal origin (e.g. vegetarian cheese is made using biosynthetic chymosin rather than traditional rennin from calves' stomach).

It is illegal to claim on a label or in advertising that a food is capable of preventing, treating or curing a disease unless it has a specific Product Licence under the Medicines Act for use for the claimed purpose.

There is, as yet, no legal definition in the European Union of such terms as 'low in', 'reduced' and 'free from', so that such claims have to be read with caution.

Nutritional labelling

Nutritional labelling of foods is voluntary in the European Union (unlike the USA, where it is obligatory). If nutritional information is given, it must be in a standard format. The information must be given /100g (or /100 ml), and may also, optionally, be given per serving of a stated size. Again this differs from the USA, where the information must be given per serving (as defined by the regulatory authorities), and may optionally be given /100 g or /100 ml.

Table 27 Example of nutritional labelling of foods

1) standard nutritional labelling
(Group 1 – the big four)

	100 g provides	a 250 g serving provides (this is optional)
energy	812 kJ/194 kcal	2030 kJ/485 kcal
protein	11.5 g	28.8 g
carbohydrates	13.9 g	34.8 g
fat	10.7 g	26.8 g

2) Group 2 – the big eight

		100 g provides	a 250 g serving provides (this is optional)
energy		812 kJ/194 kcal	2030 kJ/485 kcal
protein		11.5 g	28.8 g
carbohydrate		13.9 g	34.8 g
	of which sugars	1.8 g	4.5 g
fat		10.7 g	26.8 g
	of which saturates	4.3 g	10.8 g
fibre		1.1 g	2.8 g
sodium		458 mg	1145 mg

3) Optional additional information

calcium	93 mg	232 mg	29 % RDA
iron	1.7 mg	4.3 mg	30 % RDA
vitamin A	114 µg	285 µg	35 % RDA
vitamin B$_1$	0.16 mg	0.4 mg	29 % RDA
vitamin B$_2$	0.17 mg	0.43 mg	27 % RDA
niacin	2.6 mg	6.5 mg	36 % RDA
vitamin B$_6$	0.12 mg	0.3 mg	15 % RDA
folic acid	22 µg	55 µg	28 % RDA
vitamin B$_{12}$	0.7 µg	1.75 µg	175 % RDA
vitamin C	4 mg	10 mg	17 % RDA

If any nutritional information is given, then the minimum that must appear is as shown in box (1) in Table 27. Box (2) in Table 27 shows the additional information that is required when a claim is made about sugars, saturated fat, fibre or sodium. Additional optional information is shown in box (3); this may be expressed as a percentage of the European Union RDA for labelling shown in Table 28.

Table 28 Reference intakes for nutritional labelling of foods in the European Union

vitamin A	800 µg
vitamin D	5 µg
vitamin E	10 mg
vitamin C	60 mg
thiamin	1.4 mg
riboflavin	1.6 mg
niacin	18 mg
vitamin B_6	2.0 mg
folate	200 µg
vitamin B_{12}	1.0 µg
biotin	150 µg
pantothenic acid	6 mg
calcium	800 mg
iodine	150 µg
iron	14 mg
magnesium	300 mg
phosphorus	800 mg
zinc	15 mg

Additives

An additive is defined as any substance not commonly regarded or used as a food, which is added to a food to affect its keeping properties, texture, consistency, appearance, taste, alkalinity, acidity, or to perform any other function. Legally the term 'additive' does not include nutrients added to enrich the food, or herbs and spices used as seasonings, or salt or yeast. However, some nutrients may be used as additives for their antioxidant properties (e.g. vitamins E and C) or as colours (e.g. vitamin B_2).

Additives may be extracted from natural sources, synthesized in the laboratory to be chemically the same as natural materials (and hence known as 'nature-identical' compounds), or they may be synthetic compounds which do not occur in nature.

Additives can be grouped according to their uses and functions, as shown in Table 29.

Table 29 Uses of food additives

Antioxidants

Colours

Emulsifiers and stabilizers

Flavours

Flour improvers and processing aids (lubricants, anti-caking agents, etc)

Humectants (to maintain moisture)

pH regulation (to control acidity)

Preservatives

Solvents

Sweeteners

The use of additives is controlled by law. In some cases, the amounts that may be used are limited, or their use is restricted to specified foods, while other additives may be used more widely. In all cases, their use is only permitted when a need has been shown, and if they are regarded as being safe – hence the term 'permitted additives'.

When laboratory testing has revealed that a high dose or intake of a substance causes some change in experimental animals, then the total amount that is permitted from all foods in the daily diet is limited (with a large safety factor). This safe amount is termed the **Acceptable Daily Intake (ADI)**, agreed by international bodies such as the World Health Organization, as well as by various national government regulatory bodies. The Acceptable Daily Intake is usually one hundredth of the *highest dose that shows no effect* when tested. When no harm can be demonstrated even at very high levels of intake (very much higher than would be used in foods), then the substance may be used without any limitation, although the intensity of colour and flavour usually limit the amounts of these additives used in foods.

Permitted food additives have been classified according to their uses, and have been assigned serial numbers which may legally be used on food labels as well as, or instead of, their sometimes complex chemical names. Numbers with the prefix 'E-' are those additives permitted throughout the European Union, and covered by specific EU legislation. In addition, some compounds are permitted in Britain and some other countries, but are not covered by EU legislation; these have numbers without the 'E-' prefix. The list of permitted additives is shown in Table 30.

Table 30 Permitted food additives in the European Union (Those without the prefix E- are permitted in UK but not throughout the EU)

Colouring materials

Used to make food more colourful and attractive, or to replace colour lost in processing

Yellow and orange colours

E-100	Curcumin
E-101	Riboflavin, riboflavin phosphate (vitamin B$_2$)
E-102	Tartrazine (= FD&C Yellow no 5)
E-104	Quinoline yellow
107	Yellow 2G
E-110	Sunset yellow FCF or orange yellow S (= FD&C Yellow no 6)

Red colours

E-120	Cochineal or carminic acid
E-122	Carmoisine or azorubine
E-123	Amaranth
E-124	Ponceau 4R or cochineal red A
E-127	Erythrosine BS (= FD&C Red no 3)
E-128	Red 2G
E-129	Allura red (= FD&C Red no 40)

Blue colours

E-131	Patent blue V
E-132	Indigo carmine or indigotine (= FD&C Blue no 2)
E-133	Brilliant blue FCF (= FD&C Blue no 1)

Green colours

E-140	(i) Chlorophylls, the natural green colour of leaves (ii) chlorophyllins
E-141	Copper complexes of (i) chlorophylls, (ii) chlorophyllins
E-142	Green S or acid brilliant green BS

Brown and black colours

E-150a	Plain caramel (made from sugar in the kitchen)
E-150b	Caustic sulphite caramel
E-150c	Ammonia caramel
E150d	Sulphite ammonia caramel
E-151	Black PN or brilliant black BN
E-153	Carbon black or vegetable carbon (charcoal)
E-154	Brown FK
E-155	Brown HT (Chocolate brown HT)

Derivatives of carotene

E-160(a)	(i) Mixed carotenes, (ii) β-carotene
E-160(b)	Annatto, bixin, norbixin
E-160(c)	Paprika extract, capsanthin or capsorubin
E-160(d)	Lycopene
E-160(e)	β-apo-8'-carotenal (vitamin A active)
E-160(f)	Ethyl ester of β-apo-8'-carotenoic acid

Other plant colours

E-161(a)	Flavoxanthin
E-161(b)	Lutein
E-161(c)	Cryptoxanthin
E-161(d)	Rubixanthin
E-161(e)	Violaxanthin
E-161(f)	Rhodoxanthin
E-161(g)	Canthaxanthin
E-162	Beetroot red or betanin
E-163	Anthocyanins (the pigments of many plants)

Inorganic compounds used as colours

E-170	(i) Calcium carbonate (chalk), (ii) calcium hydrogen carbonate
E-171	Titanium dioxide
E-172	Iron oxides & hydroxides
E-173	Aluminium
E-174	Silver
E-175	Gold
E-180	Pigment rubine or lithol rubine BK

Preservatives

Compounds that protect foods against microbes that cause spoilage and food poisoning. They increase the safe storage life of foods.

Sorbic acid and its salts

E-200	Sorbic acid
E-201	Sodium sorbate
E-202	Potassium sorbate
E-203	Calcium sorbate

Benzoic acid and its salts

E-210	Benzoic acid (occurs naturally in many fruits)
E-211	Sodium benzoate
E-212	Potassium benzoate
E-213	Calcium benzoate
E-214	Ethyl *p*-hydroxybenzoate
E-215	Ethyl *p*-hydroxybenzoate sodium salt
E-216	Propyl *p*-hydroxybenzoate
E-217	Propyl *p*-hydroxybenzoate sodium salt
E-218	Methyl *p*-hydroxybenzoate
E-219	Methyl *p*-hydroxybenzoate sodium salt

Sulphur dioxide and its salts

E-220	Sulphur dioxide (also used to prevent browning of raw peeled potatoes)
E-221	Sodium sulphite
E-222	Sodium hydrogen sulphite
E-223	Sodium metabisulphite
E-224	Potassium metabisulphite
E-226	Calcium sulphite
E-227	Calcium hydrogen sulphite
E-228	Potassium hydrogen sulphite

Biphenyl and its derivatives

E-230	Biphenyl or diphenyl (for surface treatment of citrus fruits)
E-231	Orthophenylphenol (2-Hydroxybiphenyl) (for surface treatment of citrus fruits)
E-232	Sodium orthophenylphenol (sodium biphenyl-2-yl oxide)

Other preservatives

E-233	2-(Thiazol-4-yl) benzimidazole (thiobendazole) (for surface treatment of citrus fruits and bananas)
E-234	Nisin
E-235	Natamycin (NATA) (for surface treatment of cheeses and dried cured sausages)
E-239	Hexamethylene tetramine (hexamine)
E-242	Dimethyl dicarbonate
E-912	Montan acid esters (for surface treatment of citrus fruits)
E-914	Oxidized polyethylene wax (for surface treatment of citrus fruits)

Pickling salts

E-249	Potassium nitrite
E-250	Sodium nitrite
E-251	Sodium nitrate
E-252	Potassium nitrate (saltpetre)

Acids and their salts

Used as flavourings and as buffers to control the acidity of foods, in addition to their antimicrobial properties.

E-260	Acetic acid
E-261	Potassium acetate
E-262	(i) Sodium acetate, (ii) sodium hydrogen acetate (sodium diacetate)
E-263	Calcium acetate
E-270	Lactic acid
E-280	Propionic acid
E-281	Sodium propionate
E-282	Calcium propionate
E-283	Potassium propionate
E-284	Boric acid (as preservative in caviare)
E-285	Sodium tetraborate (borax) (as preservative in caviare)
E-290	Carbon dioxide
E-296	Malic acid
E-297	Fumaric acid

Antioxidants

Compounds used to prevent fatty foods going rancid, and to protect fat-soluble vitamins (A, D, E and K) against the damaging effects of oxidation.

Vitamin C and derivatives

E-300	L-Ascorbic acid (vitamin C)
E-301	Sodium-L-ascorbate
E-302	Calcium-L-ascorbate
E-304	(i) Ascorbyl palmitate, (ii) ascorbyl stearate
E-315	Erythorbic acid (*iso*-ascorbic acid)
E-316	Sodium erythorbate (sodium *iso*-ascorbate)

Vitamin E

E-306	Natural extracts rich in tocopherols
E-307	Synthetic α-tocopherol
E-308	Synthetic γ-tocopherol
E-309	Synthetic δ-tocopherol

Other antioxidants

E-310	Propyl gallate
E-311	Octyl gallate
E-312	Dodecyl gallate
E-320	Butylated hydroxyanisole (BHA)
E-321	Butylated hydroxytoluene (BHT)
E-322	Lecithins

More acids and their salts

Used as flavourings and as buffers to control the acidity of foods, in addition to other special uses

Salts of lactic acid (E270)

E-325	Sodium lactate
E-326	Potassium lactate
E-327	Calcium lactate
E-585	Ferrous lactate

Citric acid, its salts and esters

E-330	Citric acid (formed in the body, and present in many fruits)
E-331	(i) Monosodium citrate, (ii) disodium citrate, (iii) trisodium citrate
E-332	(i) Monopotassium citrate, (ii) dipotassium citrate, (iii) tripotassium citrate
E-333	(i) Monocalcium citrate, (ii) dicalcium citrate, (iii) tricalcium citrate
E-1505	Triethyl citrate

Tartaric acid and its salts

E-334	L(+)Tartaric acid (tartaric acid occurs naturally; as well as their properties as acids, tartrates are often used as sequestrants and emulsifying agents
E-335	(i) Monosodium tartrate, (ii) disodium tartrate
E-336	(i) Monopotassium tartrate (cream of tartar), (ii) dipotassium tartrate
E-337	Sodium potassium tartrate

Phosphoric acid and its salts

E-338	Phosphoric acid
E-339	(i) Monosodium phosphate, (ii) disodium phosphate, (iii) trisodium phosphate
E-340	(i) Monopotassium phosphate, (ii) dipotassium phosphate, (iii) tripotassium phosphate
E-341	(i) Monocalcium phosphate, (ii) dicalcium phosphate, (iii) tricalcium phosphate
E-450	Diphosphates: (i) disodium diphosphate, (ii) trisodium diphosphate, (iii) tetrasodium diphosphate, (iv) dipotassium diphosphate, (v) tetrapotassium diphosphate, (vi) dicalcium diphosphate, (vii) calcium dihydrogen diphosphate
E-451	Triphosphates: (i) pentasodium triphosphate, (ii) pentapotassium triphosphate
E-452	Polyphosphates: (i) sodium polyphosphate, (ii) potassium polyphosphate, (iii) sodium calcium polyphosphate, (iv) calcium polyphosphate
E-540	Dicalcium diphosphate
E-541	Sodium aluminium phosphate, acidic
E-542	Edible bone phosphates (bone meal, used as anticaking agent)
E-544	Calcium polyphosphates (used as anticaking agent)
E-545	Ammonium polyphosphates (used as anticaking agent)

Salts of malic acid (E-296)

E-350	Sodium malate
E-351	Potassium malate
E-352	Calcium malate

Other acids and their salts

E-353	Metatartaric acid
E-354	Calcium tartrate
E-355	Adipic acid
E-356	Sodium adipate
E-357	Potassium adipate
E-363	Succinic acid
E-370	1,4-Heptonolactone
E-375	Nicotinic acid
E-380	Triammonium citrate
E-381	Ammonium ferric citrate
E-385	Calcium disodium EDTA

Emulsifiers and stabilisers

Used to enable oils and fats to mix with water, to give a smooth and creamy texture to food, and slow the staling of baked goods. Many of these compounds are also used to make jellies.

Alginates

E-400	Alginic acid (derived from seaweed)
E-401	Sodium alginate
E-402	Potassium alginate
E-403	Ammonium alginate
E-404	Calcium alginate
E-405	Propane-1,2-diol alginate

Other plant gums

E-406	Agar (derived from seaweed)
E-407	Carrageenan (derived from the seaweed Irish moss)
E-410	Locust bean gum (carob gum)
E-412	Guar gum
E-413	Tragacanth
E-414	Gum acacia (gum Arabic)
E-415	Xanthan gum
E-416	Karaya gum

E-417	Tara gums
E-418	Gellan gums

Fatty acid derivatives

E-430	polyoxyethylene (8) stearate
E-431	polyoxyethylene (40) stearate
E-432	polyoxyethylene (20) sorbitan monolaurate (Polysorbate 20)
E-433	polyoxyethylene (20) sorbitan mono-oleate (Polysorbate 80)
E-434	polyoxyethylene (20) sorbitan monopalmitate (Polysorbate 40)
E-435	polyoxyethylene (20) sorbitan monostearate (Polysorbate 60)
E-436	polyoxyethylene (20) sorbitan tristearate (Polysorbate 65)

Pectin and derivatives

E-440	(i) Pectin, (ii) amidated pectin (pectin occurs in many fruits, and is often added to jam to help it set)

Other compounds

E-322	Lecithins
E-442	Ammonium phosphatides
E-444	Sucrose acetate isobutyrate
E-445	Glycerol esters of wood rosins

Cellulose and derivatives

E-460	(i) Microcrystalline cellulose, (ii) powdered cellulose
E-461	Methyl cellulose
E-463	Hydroxypropyl cellulose
E-464	Hydroxypropylmethyl cellulose
E-465	Ethylmethyl cellulose
E-466	Carboxymethylcellulose, sodium carboxymethylcellulose

Salts or esters of fatty acids

E-470a	Sodium, potassium and calcium salts of fatty acids
E-470b	Magnesium salts of fatty acids
E-471	Mono-and di-glycerides of fatty acids
E-472a	Acetic acid esters of mono- and diglycerides of fatty acids

E-472b	Lactic acid esters of mono- and diglycerides of fatty acids
E-472c	Citric acid esters of mono- and diglycerides of fatty acids
E-472d	Tartaric acid esters of mono- and diglycerides of fatty acids
E-472e	Mono- and diacetyl tartaric esters of mono- and diglycerides of fatty acids
E-472f	Mixed acetic and tartaric acid esters of mono- and diglycerides of fatty acids
E-473	Sucrose esters of fatty acids
E-474	Sucroglycerides
E-475	Polyglycerol esters of fatty acids
E-476	Polyglycerol esters of polycondensed esters of castor oil (polyglycerol polyricinoleate)
E-477	Propane-1,2-diol esters of fatty acids
E-478	Lactylated fatty acid esters of glycerol and propane 1,2-diol
E-479b	Thermally oxidized soya bean oil interacted with mono- and diglycerides of fatty acids
E-481	Sodium stearoyl-2-lactylate
E-482	Calcium stearoyl-2-lactylate
E-483	Stearyl tartrate
E-491	Sorbitan monostearate
E-492	Sorbitan tristearate
E-493	Sorbitan monolaurate
E-494	Sorbitan mono-oleate
E-495	Sorbitan monopalmitate
E-1518	Glyceryl triacetate (triacetin)

Acids and salts used for special purposes

Buffers, emulsifying salts, sequestrants, stabilizers, raising agents, anti-caking agents

Carbonates

E-500	(i) Sodium carbonate, (ii) sodium bicarbonate (sodium hydrogen carbonate), (iii) sodium sesquicarbonate
E-501	(i) Potassium carbonate, (ii) potassium bicarbonate (potassium hydrogen carbonate)
E-503	(i) Ammonium carbonate, (ii) ammonium hydrogen carbonate
E-504	(i) Magnesium carbonate, (ii) magnesium hydrogen carbonate (magnesium hydroxide carbonate)

Hydrochloric acid and its salts

E-507	Hydrochloric acid (ordinary salt is sodium chloride)
E-508	Potassium chloride (sometimes used as a replacement for ordinary salt)
E-509	Calcium chloride
E-510	Ammonium chloride
E-511	Magnesium chloride
E-512	Stannous chloride

Sulphuric acid and its salts

E-513	Sulphuric acid
E-514	(i) Sodium sulphate, (ii) sodium hydrogen sulphate
E-515	(i) Potassium sulphate, (ii) potassium hydrogen sulphate
E-516	Calcium sulphate
E-517	Ammonium sulphate
E-518	Magnesium sulphate
E-520	Aluminium sulphate
E-521	Aluminium sodium sulphate
E-522	Aluminium potassium sulphate
E-523	Aluminium ammonium sulphate

Alkalis — Used as bases to neutralize acids in foods

E-524	Sodium hydroxide
E-525	Potassium hydroxide
E-526	Calcium hydroxide
E-527	Ammonium hydroxide
E-528	Magnesium hydroxide
E-529	Calcium oxide
E-530	Magnesium oxide

Other salts

E-535	Sodium ferrocyanide
E-536	Potassium ferrocyanide
E-538	Calcium ferrocyanide
E-540	Dicalcium diphosphate
E-541	Sodium aluminium phosphate, acidic

97

Compounds used as anti-caking agents, and other uses

E-542	Edible bone phosphate (bone meal)
E-544	Calcium polyphosphates
E-545	Ammonium polyphosphates

Silicon salts

E-551	Silicon dioxide (silica, sand)
E-552	Calcium silicate
E-553a	(i) Magnesium silicate, (ii) magnesium trisilicate
E-553b	talc
E-554	Sodium aluminium silicate
E-555	Potassium aluminium silicate
E-556	Calcium aluminium silicate

Other compounds

E-558	Bentonite
E-559	Kaolin (aluminium silicate)
E-570	Fatty acids
E-572	Magnesium stearate
E-574	Gluconic acid
E-575	Glucono-δ-lactone
E-576	Sodium gluconate
E-577	Potassium gluconate
E-578	Calcium gluconate
E-579	Ferrous gluconate
E-585	Ferrous lactate

Compounds used as flavour enhancers

E-620	L-Glutamic acid (a natural amino acid)
E-621	Monosodium glutamate (MSG)
E-622	Monopotassium glutamate
E-623	Calcium diglutamate
E-624	Monoammonium glutamate
E-625	Magnesium diglutamate
E-626	Guanylic acid
E-627	Disodium guanylate
E-628	Dipotassium guanylate
E-629	Calcium guanylate
E-630	Inosinic acid

E-631	Disodium inosinate
E-632	Dipotassium inosinate
E-633	Calcium inosinate
E-634	Calcium 5'-ribonucleotides
E-635	Disodium 5-ribonucleotides
E-636	Maltol
E-637	Ethyl maltol
E-640	Glycine and its sodium salt (a natural amino acid)
E-900	Dimethylpolysiloxane

Compounds used as glazing agents

E-901	Beeswax
E-902	Candelilla wax
E-903	Carnauba wax
E-904	Shellac
E-912	Montan acid esters
E-914	Oxidized polyethylene wax

Compounds used to treat flour

E-920	L-Cysteine hydrochloride (a natural amino acid)
924	Potassium bromate
925	Chlorine
926	Chlorine dioxide
927	Azo-dicarbamide

Propellant gases

E-938	Argon
E-939	Helium
E-941	Nitrogen
E-942	Nitrous oxide
E-948	Oxygen

Sweeteners and sugar alcohols

E-420	(i) Sorbitol, (ii) sorbitol syrup
E-421	Mannitol
E-422	Glycerol
E-927a	Azodicarbonamide
E-927b	Carbamide
E-950	Acesulfame K

E-951	Aspartame
E-952	Cyclamic acid and its sodium and calcium salts
E-953	Isomalt
E-954	Saccharine and its sodium, potassium and calcium salts
E-957	Thaumatin
E-959	Neohesperidin didihydrochalcone
E-965	(i) Maltitol, (ii) maltitol syrup
E-966	Lactitol
E-967	Xylitol

Miscellaneous compounds

E-999	Quillaia extract
E-1105	Lysozyme
E-1200	Polydextrose
E-1201	Polyvinyl pyrrolidone
E-1202	Polyvinyl polypyrrolidone
E-1505	Triethyl citrate
E-1518	Glyceryl triacetate (triacetin)

Modified starches

E-1404	Oxidized starch
E-1410	Monostarch phosphate
E-1412	Distarch phosphate
E-1413	Phosphated distarch phosphate
E-1414	Acetylated distarch phosphate
E-1420	Acetylated starch
E-1422	Acetylated starch adipate
E-1440	Hydroxypropyl starch
E-1442	Hydroxypropyl distarch phosphate
E-1450	Starch sodium octanoyl succinate

F) Height, weight and growth

Figure 6 shows the results of a study of three-quarters of a million people who were studied over a 15 year period. It is obvious from this figure that those who were seriously overweight were almost twice as likely to die during the study period as those who were not overweight.

From the results of studies like this, we can derive a range of desirable weights for height, as the weights at which there is least chance of premature death. These ranges for adults are shown in Tables 31 and 32.

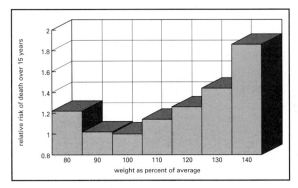

Figure 6 The effect of body weight on mortality

Table 31
Desirable ranges of weight for height for adults, metric units

height	desirable range of weight		
cm	kg		kg
150	45.0	–	56.3
152	46.2	–	57.8
154	47.4	–	59.3
156	48.7	–	60.8
158	49.9	–	62.4
160	51.2	–	64.0
162	52.5	–	65.6
164	53.8	–	67.2
166	55.1	–	68.9
168	56.4	–	70.6
170	57.8	–	72.3
172	59.2	–	74.0
174	60.6	–	75.7
176	62.0	–	77.4
178	63.4	–	79.2
180	64.8	–	81.0
182	66.2	–	82.8
184	67.7	–	84.6
186	69.2	–	86.5
188	70.7	–	88.4
190	72.2	–	90.3
192	73.7	–	92.2
194	75.3	–	94.1
196	76.8	–	96.0
198	78.4	–	98.0

Table 32 Desirable ranges of weight for height for adults, Imperial units

height		weight			weight	
ft	in	st	lb		st	lb
4	11	7	0	–	8	10
5	0	7	3	–	9	1
5	1	7	7	–	9	5
5	2	7	10	–	9	9
5	3	8	0	–	10	0
5	4	8	3	–	10	4
5	5	8	7	–	10	9
5	6	8	11	–	10	13
5	7	9	0	–	11	4
5	8	9	4	–	11	9
5	9	9	8	–	11	13
5	10	9	12	–	12	4
5	11	10	2	–	12	9
6	0	10	6	–	13	0
6	1	10	10	–	13	5
6	2	11	0	–	13	11
6	3	11	4	–	14	2
6	4	11	8	–	14	7
6	5	11	13	–	14	12
6	6	12	3	–	15	4

We can simplify these tables, and rather than listing the upper and lower limits of the desirable range of weight for each height, calculate a **Body Mass Index (BMI**, sometimes also called Quetelet's Index, after Quetelet, who first devised it).

$$\text{Body Mass Index} = \frac{\text{weight (in kg)}}{\text{height}^2 \text{ (in m)}}$$

Table 33 shows the classification of ranges of Body Mass Index. These ranges are only applicable to adults, and not children. There is some evidence that the desirable range (shown in Table 33 as BMI 25–30) could be increased by one unit for each decade of life after 35, as shown in Table 34.

Table 34 Desirable ranges of Body Mass Index with age

age	BMI
19–24	19–24
25–34	20–25
35–44	21–26
45–54	22–27
55–64	23–28
over 65	24–29

Table 33 Ranges of Body Mass Index for adults

Body mass index		
< 16	severe protein-energy malnutrition	
16–17	moderately severe protein-energy malnutrition	
17–18.4	moderate protein-energy malnutrition	
18.4–20	underweight but acceptable	
20–25	desirable/ideal range	
25–27	acceptable but not desirable	
27–30	overweight	5–15 kg overweight
30–40	obesity	15–25 kg overweight
> 40	severe obesity	> 25 kg overweight

The ranges of weight and height from birth to age 18 are shown in Tables 35–38.

Table 35 Height and weight for age, boys, metric units

For infants under 3 years, figures (in italics) show length lying down, not height standing up.

age	weight			height		
	kg			cm		
birth	2.54	–	4.15	*46.4*	–	*54.4*
1 m	3.16	–	5.38	*50.4*	–	*58.6*
3 m	4.43	–	7.37	*56.7*	–	*65.4*
6 m	6.20	–	9.46	*63.4*	–	*72.3*
9 m	7.52	–	10.93	*68.0*	–	*77.1*
1 y	8.43	–	11.99	*71.7*	–	*81.2*
1.5 y	9.59	–	13.44	*77.5*	–	*88.1*
2 y	10.54	–	14.7	*82.3*	–	*93.8*
2.5 y	11.44	–	15.97	*87.0*	–	*98.7*
3 y	12.1	–	17.8	89.0	–	102.0
3.5 y	12.8	–	18.9	92.5	–	106.1
4 y	13.6	–	20.3	95.8	–	109.9
4.5 y	14.5	–	21.6	98.9	–	113.5
5 y	15.3	–	23.1	102.0	–	117.0
5.5 y	16.1	–	24.7	104.9	–	120.3
6 y	16.9	–	26.3	107.7	–	123.5
6.5 y	17.8	–	28.2	110.4	–	126.6
7 y	18.6	–	30.1	113.0	–	129.7
7.5 y	18.6	–	30.1	115.6	–	132.7
8 y	20.4	–	34.5	118.1	–	135.7
8.5 y	21.3	–	37.0	120.5	–	138.8
9 y	22.3	–	39.6	122.9	–	141.8
9.5 y	23.3	–	42.4	125.3	–	144.9
10 y	24.3	–	45.3	127.7	–	148.1
10.5 y	25.5	–	48.3	130.1	–	151.5
11 y	26.8	–	51.5	132.6	–-	154.9
11.5 y	28.2	–	54.7	135.0	–	158.5
12 y	29.9	–	58.1	137.6	–	162.3
12.5 y	31.6	–	61.5	140.2	–	166.1
13 y	33.6	–	65.0	142.9	–	169.8
13.5 y	35.9	–	68.5	145.7	–	173.4
14 y	38.2	–	72.1	148.8	–	176.7
14.5 y	40.7	–	75.7	152.0	–	179.5
15 y	43.1	–	79.1	155.2	–	181.9
15.5 y	45.5	–	82.5	158.3	–	183.9
16 y	47.4	–	85.6	161.1	–	185.4
16.5 y	49.8	–	88.6	163.4	–	186.6
17 y	51.5	–	91.3	164.9	–	187.3
17.5 y	52.9	–	93.7	165.6	–	187.6
18 y	54.0	–	95.8	165.7	–	187.6

Table 36 Height and weight for age, boys, Imperial units

For infants under 3 years, figures (in italics) show length lying down, not height standing up.

age	weight						height				
	st	lb		st	lb		ft	in		ft	in
birth	0	5.6	–	0	9.1		*1*	*6.3*	–	*1*	*9.4*
1 m	0	7.0	–	0	11.9		*1*	*7.8*	–	*1*	*11.1*
3 m	0	9.8	–	1	0.2		*1*	*10.3*	–	*2*	*1.7*
6 m	0	13.7	–	1	4.8		*2*	*1.0*	–	*2*	*4.5*
9 m	1	0.6	–	1	8.1		*2*	*2.8*	–	*2*	*6.4*
1 y	1	2.6	–	1	10.4		*2*	*4.2*	–	*2*	*8.0*
1.5 y	1	5.1	–	1	13.6		*2*	*6.5*	–	*2*	*10.7*
2 y	1	7.2	–	2	0.4		*2*	*8.4*	–	*3*	*0.9*
2.5 y	1	9.2	–	2	3.2		*2*	*10.3*	–	*3*	*2.9*
3 y	1	10.7	–	2	7.2		2	11.0	–	3	4.2
3.5 y	1	12.2	–	2	9.6		3	0.4	–	3	5.8
4 y	1	14.0	–	2	12.7		3	1.7	–	3	7.3
4.5 y	1	15.9	–	2	15.6		3	2.9	–	3	8.7
5 y	2	1.7	–	3	2.9		3	4.2	–	3	10.1
5.5 y	2	3.5	–	3	6.4		3	5.3	–	3	11.4
6 y	2	5.2	–	3	9.9		3	6.4	–	4	0.6
6.5 y	2	7.2	–	3	14.1		3	7.5	–	4	1.8
7 y	2	9.0	–	4	2.3		3	8.5	–	4	3.1
7.5 y	2	9.0	–	4	2.3		3	9.5	–	4	4.2
8 y	2	12.9	–	4	12.0		3	10.5	–	4	5.4
8.5 y	2	14.9	–	5	1.5		3	11.4	–	4	6.6
9 y	3	1.1	–	5	7.2		4	0.4	–	4	7.8
9.5 y	3	3.3	–	5	13.4		4	1.3	–	4	9.0
10 y	3	5.5	–	6	3.8		4	2.3	–	4	10.3
10.5 y	3	8.2	–	6	10.4		4	3.2	–	4	11.6
11 y	3	11.0	–	7	1.4		4	4.2	–	5	1.0
11.5 y	3	14.1	–	7	8.5		4	5.1	–	5	2.4
12 y	4	1.9	–	8	0.0		4	6.2	–	5	3.9
12.5 y	4	5.6	–	8	7.5		4	7.2	–	5	5.4
13 y	4	10.0	–	8	15.2		4	8.3	–	5	6.9
13.5 y	4	15.1	–	9	6.9		4	9.4	–	5	8.3
14 y	5	4.1	–	9	14.8		4	10.6	–	5	9.6
14.5 y	5	9.6	–	10	6.7		4	11.8	–	5	10.7
15 y	5	14.9	–	10	14.2		5	1.1	–	5	11.6
15.5 y	6	4.2	–	11	5.7		5	2.3	–	6	0.4
16 y	6	8.4	–	11	12.5		5	3.4	–	6	1.0
16.5 y	6	13.7	–	12	3.2		5	4.3	–	6	1.5
17 y	7	1.4	–	12	9.1		5	4.9	–	6	1.7
17.5 y	7	4.5	–	12	14.4		5	5.2	–	6	1.9
18 y	7	6.9	–	13	3.0		5	5.2	–	6	1.9

Table 37 Height and weight for age, girls, metric units

For infants under 3 years, figures (in italics) show length lying down, not height standing up.

age	weight			height		
	kg			cm		
birth	2.36	–	3.81	*45.4*	–	*52.9*
1 m	2.97	–	4.92	*49.2*	–	*56.9*
3 m	4.18	–	6.74	*55.4*	–	*63.4*
6 m	5.79	–	8.73	*61.8*	–	*70.2*
9 m	7.00	–	10.17	*66.1*	–	*75.0*
1 y	7.84	–	11.24	*69.8*	–	*79.1*
1.5 y	8.92	–	12.76	*76.0*	–	*86.1*
2 y	9.87	–	14.08	*81.3*	–	*92.0*
2.5 y	10.78	–	15.35	*86.0*	–	*96.9*
3 y	11.6	–	17.2	88.3	–	100.6
3.5 y	12.4	–	18.6	91.7	–	104.5
4 y	13.1	–	19.9	95.0	–	108.3
4.5 y	13.8	–	21.2	98.1	–	112.0
5 y	14.6	–	22.6	101.1	–	115.6
5.5 y	15.3	–	24.1	103.9	–	119.2
6 y	16.1	–	25.8	106.6	–	122.7
6.5 y	16.9	–	27.6	109.2	–	126.1
7 y	17.7	–	29.7	111.8	–	129.5
7.5 y	18.6	–	32.1	114.4	–	132.9
8 y	19.6	–	34.7	116.9	–	136.2
8.5 y	20.7	–	37.6	119.5	–	139.6
9 y	21.8	–	40.6	122.1	–	142.9
9.5 y	23.1	–	43.9	124.8	–	146.2
10 y	24.4	–	47.2	127.5	–	149.5
10.5 y	25.8	–	50.6	130.4	–	152.8
11 y	27.2	–	54.0	133.5	–	156.2
11.5 y	28.8	–	57.4	136.6	–	159.5
12 y	30.5	–	60.8	139.8	–	162.7
12.5 y	32.3	–	64.1	142.7	–	165.6
13 y	34.1	–	67.3	145.2	–	168.1
13.5 y	36.0	–	70.3	147.2	–	170.0
14 y	37.8	–	73.1	148.7	–	171.3
14.5 y	39.5	–	75.6	149.7	–	172.2
15 y	41.0	–	77.8	150.5	–	172.8
15.5 y	42.3	–	79.6	151.1	–	173.1
16 y	43.4	–	81.0	151.6	–	173.3
16.5 y	44.2	–	81.9	152.2	–	173.4
17 y	44.7	–	82.5	152.7	–	173.5
17.5 y	45.1	–	82.6	153.2	–	173.5
18 y	45.3	–	82.5	153.6	–	173.6

Table 38   Height and weight for age, girls, Imperial units

For infants under 3 years, figures (in italics) show length lying down, not height standing up.

age	weight				height			
	st	lb	st	lb	ft	in	ft	in
birth	0	5.2	–	0	8.4	*1*	*5.9*	–	*1*	*8.8*
1 m	0	6.5	–	0	10.8	*1*	*7.4*	–	*1*	*10.4*
3 m	0	9.2	–	0	14.8	*1*	*9.8*	–	*2*	*1.0*
6 m	0	12.8	–	1	3.2	*2*	*0.3*	–	*2*	*3.6*
9 m	0	15.4	–	1	6.4	*2*	*2.0*	–	*2*	*5.5*
1 y	1	1.3	–	1	8.8	*2*	*3.5*	–	*2*	*7.1*
1.5 y	1	3.6	–	1	12.1	*2*	*5.9*	–	*2*	*9.9*
2 y	1	5.7	–	1	15.0	*2*	*8.0*	–	*3*	*0.2*
2.5 y	1	7.7	–	2	1.8	*2*	*9.9*	–	*3*	*2.1*
3 y	1	9.6	–	2	5.9	2	10.8	–	3	3.6
3.5 y	1	11.3	–	2	9.0	3	0.1	–	3	5.1
4 y	1	12.9	–	2	11.8	3	1.4	–	3	6.6
4.5 y	1	14.4	–	2	14.7	3	2.6	–	3	8.1
5 y	2	0.2	–	3	1.8	3	3.8	–	3	9.5
5.5 y	2	1.7	–	3	5.1	3	4.9	–	3	10.9
6 y	2	3.5	–	3	8.8	3	6.0	–	4	0.3
6.5 y	2	5.2	–	3	12.8	3	7.0	–	4	1.6
7 y	2	7.0	–	4	1.4	3	8.0	–	4	3.0
7.5 y	2	9.0	–	4	6.7	3	9.0	–	4	4.3
8 y	2	11.2	–	4	12.4	3	10.0	–	4	5.6
8.5 y	2	13.6	–	5	2.8	3	11.0	–	4	7.0
9 y	3	0.0	–	5	9.4	4	0.1	–	4	8.3
9.5 y	3	2.9	–	6	0.7	4	1.1	–	4	9.6
10 y	3	5.7	–	6	8.0	4	2.2	–	4	10.9
10.5 y	3	8.8	–	6	15.5	4	3.3	–	5	0.2
11 y	3	11.9	–	7	6.9	4	4.6	–	5	1.5
11.5 y	3	15.4	–	7	14.4	4	5.8	–	5	2.8
12 y	4	3.2	–	8	5.9	4	7.0	–	5	4.1
12.5 y	4	7.1	–	8	13.2	4	8.2	–	5	5.2
13 y	4	11.1	–	9	4.2	4	9.2	–	5	6.2
13.5 y	4	15.3	–	9	10.8	4	10.0	–	5	6.9
14 y	5	3.3	–	10	1.0	4	10.5	–	5	7.4
14.5 y	5	7.0	–	10	6.5	4	10.9	–	5	7.8
15 y	5	10.3	–	10	11.4	4	11.3	–	5	8.0
15.5 y	5	13.2	–	10	15.3	4	11.5	–	5	8.1
16 y	5	15.6	–	11	2.4	4	11.7	–	5	8.2
16.5 y	6	1.4	–	11	4.4	4	11.9	–	5	8.3
17 y	6	2.5	–	11	5.7	5	0.1	–	5	8.3
17.5 y	6	3.3	–	11	5.9	5	0.3	–	5	8.3
18 y	6	3.8	–	11	5.7	5	0.5	–	5	8.3

G) Miscellaneous tables

Table 39   Prefixes for multiples and submultiples of units

		name	symbol
a million million times	x 10^{12}	tera	T
a thousand million times	x 10^9	giga	G
a million times	x 10^6	mega	M
a thousand times	x 10^3	kilo	k
a hundred times	x 10^2	centa	ca
ten times	x 10	deca	da
one tenth	x 10^{-1}	deci	d
one hundredth	x 10^{-2}	centi	c
one thousandth	x 10^{-3}	milli	m
one millionth	x 10^{-6}	micro	μ (or mc)
one thousand millionth	x 10^{-9}	nano	n
one million millionth	x 10^{-12}	pico	p

Table 40   The equivalence of Imperial and metric units

metric equivalents of Imperial units	Imperial equivalents of metric units
1 oz = 28.35 g (approximate to 30 g)	1 g = 0.035 oz
1 lb (16 oz) = 454 g (approximate to 450 g)	100 g = 3.5 oz
1 fluid oz = 28.35 ml (approximate to 30 ml)	1 ml = 0.035 fluid oz
1 pint (20 fluid oz) = 568 ml (approximate to 570 ml)	1 l = 25 fluid oz = 1.75 pints

Table 41   Metric equivalents of Imperial weights

Imperial (oz)	approximate metric (g)	precise metric (g)
1	30	28.35
2	60	56.70
3	85	85.05
4	110	113.40
5	140	141.75
6	170	170.10
7	200	198.45
8	230	226.80
16 (1 lb)	450	453.60

Table 42 Imperial equivalents of metric weights

metric (g)	approximate Imperial (oz)	precise Imperial (oz)
10	$^1/_3$	0.35
20	$^2/_3$	0.71
30	1	1.05
40	1 $^1/_2$	1.41
50	1 $^3/_4$	1.76
60	2	2.12
70	2 $^1/_2$	2.47
80	3	2.82
90	3	3.17
100	3 $^1/_2$	3.53
150	5	5.29
200	7	7.05
250	9	8.82
300	10 $^1/_2$	10.58
350	12 $^1/_3$	12.34
400	14	14.11
450	16	15.87
500	17$^1/_2$ (1 lb 1$^1/_2$ oz)	17.64
1000	35$^1/_4$ (2 lb 3$^1/_4$ oz)	35.27

Table 43 Metric equivalents of Imperial volumes

Imperial (fluid oz)		approximate metric (ml)	precise metric (ml)
1		30	28.4
2		60	56.7
3		85	85.1
4		110	113.4
5	$^1/_4$ pint	140	141.8
6		170	170.1
7		200	198.5
8		230	226.8
9		260	255.2
10	$^1/_2$ pint	280	283.5
15	$^3/_4$ pint	425	425.3
20	1 pint	570	567.0
40	1 quart	1140 (1.14 l)	1134.0
80	$^1/_2$ gallon	2270 (2.27 l)	2268.0
160	1 gallon	4500 (4.5 l)	4536.0

Table 44 Imperial equivalents of metric volumes

metric (ml)	approximate Imperial (fluid oz)	precise Imperial (fluid oz)	
100 (1 dl)	3^{1}/$_{2}$	3.52	
250	9	8.82	
500	18	17.64	
1000 (1 l)	35^{1}/$_{4}$	35.27	1 ^{3}/$_{4}$ pints

Table 45 Equivalence of household and American measures

	metric	Imperial
^{1}/$_{2}$ teaspoon	2.5 ml	–
1 teaspoon	5 ml	–
1 dessertspoon (= 2 teaspoons)	10 ml	–
1 standard measuring tablespoon	15 ml	–
1 traditional tablespoon (= 2 dessertspoons or 3 teaspoons in USA)	20 ml	–
1 cup (UK)	283 ml	10 fluid oz
1 cup (US)	227 ml	8 fluid oz
1 US cup of butter, margarine, granulated sugar	230 g	8 oz
1 US cup of icing sugar	150 g	5 ^{1}/$_{3}$ oz
1 US cup of flour	110 g	4 oz
1 US gallon	3.78 l	6.6 Imp pints
1 US quart	945 ml	32 fluid oz
1 US pint	470 ml	16 fluid oz

The metric scale of temperature is the Celsius scale (°C, sometimes also known as centigrade); on this scale the freezing point of water is 0°C, and boiling point is 100°C. The older Fahrenheit scale is still sometimes used – freezing point is 32°F and boiling point is 212°F.

- To convert a Fahrenheit temperature to Celsius, subtract 32, then multiply by 5/9
- To convert a Celsius temperature to Fahrenheit, multiply by 9/5, then add 32.

Electric ovens are scaled in temperature (usually Celsius, but you will still find Fahrenheit on older ovens). Gas ovens use a Regulo scale, from a low of 1/4 to a high of 10 to indicate temperature.

Table 46 Equivalence of temperatures

°C	°F	gas Regulo	
−18	0	−	*** deep freeze − for 3 months storage
−11	12	−	** freezer compartment − for 1 month storage
−4	25	−	* freezer compartment − for 1 week storage
0	32	−	freezing point of water
5	41	−	normal refrigerator
21	68	−	standard room temperature
100	212	−	boiling point of water
120	225	¼	
130	250	½	
140	275	1	very cool oven
150	300	2	cool oven
160	310	−	normal gentle frying
170	325	3	very moderate oven
180	350	4	moderate oven/normal hot frying
190	375	5	upper limit for frying
200	400	6	moderately hot oven
220	425	7	hot oven
230	450	8	
240	475	9	very hot oven
250	500	10	

Table 47 Temperatures achieved in pressure cooking

pressure above atmospheric		boiling point of water	
lb	kPa	°C	°F
0	0	100	212
5	35	109	228
10	70	115	240
15	100	121	250